Elements of Lite

Second Course

Language Handbook Worksheets
Additional Practice in Grammar, Usage, and Mechanics

*Correlated to Rules in the Language Handbook
in the Student Edition*

HOLT, RINEHART AND WINSTON

A Harcourt Education Company

Orlando • Austin • New York • San Diego • Toronto • London

Staff Credits

Associate Director: Mescal Evler

Manager of Editorial Operations: Robert R. Hoyt

Managing Editor: Bill Wahlgren

Project Editor: Katie Vignery

Component Editors: Marcia Kelley, Karen H. Kolar, James Hynes

Editorial Staff: *Associate Editors,* Kathryn Rogers, Christopher LeCluyse; *Assistant Managing Editor,* Mandy Beard; *Copyediting Manager,* Michael Neibergall; *Senior Copyeditor,* Mary Malone; *Copyeditors,* Joel Bourgeois, Jeffrey T. Holt, Suzi A. Hunn, Jane Kominek, Désirée Reid; *Editorial Coordinators,* Marie H. Price, Robert Littlefield, Mark Holland, Jill Chertudi, Tracy DeMont, Marcus Johnson; *Support Staff,* Pat Stover, Matthew Villalobos; *Word Processors,* Ruth Hooker, Margaret Sànchez, Kelly Keeley, Elizabeth Butler

Permissions: Tamara A. Blanken, Ann B. Farrar

Design: *Art Director, Book Design,* Richard Metzger; *Design Manager, Book & Media Design,* Joe Melomo

Prepress Production: Beth Prevelige, Simira Davis, Sergio Durante

Manufacturing Coordinator: Michael Roche

ISBN 0-03-073919-5

10 179   08 07

TABLE OF CONTENTS

LANGUAGE HANDBOOK 1
THE PARTS OF SPEECH

LANGUAGE HANDBOOK 2
AGREEMENT

LANGUAGE HANDBOOK 6
PHRASES

LANGUAGE HANDBOOK 7
CLAUSES

LANGUAGE HANDBOOK 8
SENTENCES

LANGUAGE HANDBOOK 9
COMPLEMENTS

LANGUAGE HANDBOOK 10
KINDS OF SENTENCES

LANGUAGE HANDBOOK 11
WRITING EFFECTIVE SENTENCES

LANGUAGE HANDBOOK 12
CAPITAL LETTERS

LANGUAGE HANDBOOK 13
PUNCTUATION

LANGUAGE HANDBOOK 14
PUNCTUATION

LANGUAGE HANDBOOK 15
PUNCTUATION

LANGUAGE HANDBOOK 16
SPELLING

LANGUAGE HANDBOOK 17
GLOSSARY OF USAGE

Elements of Literature

This booklet, *Language Handbook Worksheets,* contains practice and reinforcement copying masters that cover the material presented in the Language Handbook section of *Elements of Literature, Second Course.* The rules cited in the head of each worksheet correspond directly to the grammar, usage, and mechanics rules and instruction covered in the Language Handbook. Tests at the end of each section can be used either for assessment or as end-of-section reviews.

A separate *Answer Key* for the *Language Handbook Worksheets* provides answers or suggested responses to all items in this booklet.

LANGUAGE HANDBOOK **1** THE PARTS OF SPEECH

WORKSHEET 3 | Identifying Adjectives (Rule 1 c)

EXERCISE A   Underline each of the adjectives in the following sentences. Do not include adjectives in book and story titles. Do not include the articles *a, an,* and *the.*

> **EXAMPLE 1.** Washington Irving was one of the <u>first</u> <u>American</u> writers who won an <u>international</u> reputation.

1. Even as a <u>young</u> man, he had a <u>whimsical</u> spirit.

2. In his <u>humorous</u> book *The Sketch Book,* he says he "made many tours of discovery into foreign parts and unknown regions" of his native city.

3. *A History of New York,* his <u>first</u> book, was <u>popular</u> and <u>successful</u>.

4. His <u>quaint</u> tales of life in the rural valleys near the Hudson River are <u>delightful</u> even today.

5. Most students have heard of "Rip Van Winkle" and "The Legend of Sleepy Hollow."

6. These stories contain <u>supernatural</u> events.

7. Irving spent many <u>pleasant</u> years in England and Spain.

8. In Spain he wrote about <u>Moorish</u> legends.

9. When he returned to this country, he built a <u>comfortable</u> house that he called "Sunnyside," near Tarrytown, New York.

10. He spent the rest of his long life there, devoting himself to <u>literary</u> matters.

EXERCISE B   In the following paragraph, underline each adjective and draw an arrow to the word it modifies. Do not include the articles *a, an,* and *the.*

> **EXAMPLE** [1] Our <u>writing</u> teacher gave our class a <u>special</u> assignment.

[1] We are supposed to research haiku, which is a unique form of Japanese poetry. [2] A haiku is a short poem that expresses strong emotion or a vivid image in a few words. [3] After we have read English translations of several Japanese poems, our teacher wants us to pick our favorite poet and write a brief report. [4] Our reports must be accurate, and we will have to spend two hours in the library. [5] We don't mind, because all of us think the library is a great place for studying. [6] I am eager to start working on my subject, the famous poet Taniguchi Buson. [7] I think his poetry is wonderful. [8] The librarian can give me excellent tips on which poetry books I should research. [9] My teacher says her favorite Japanese poet is Kobayashi Issa. [10] My best friend Felicia agrees that these poets are masters.

LANGUAGE
HANDBOOK **1** THE PARTS OF SPEECH

WORKSHEET 4 | Identifying and Using Action and Helping Verbs (Rules 1 d, e, g)

EXERCISE A   Underline the verbs in each of the following sentences. Be sure to include helping verbs.

> **EXAMPLE 1.** Our football team <u>might</u> well <u>win</u> nearly every game this season.

1. The crowd arrives early for Latisha's rendition of the national anthem.
2. Last week we played Burdick School.
3. Their halfback towers above the other players.
4. Our fullback ran the ball every time.
5. During one play he dodged around left end.
6. Our team did not block effectively, however.
7. Our girls' soccer team will defend its title as the state's best.
8. Sarah Chang has scored twenty-three goals in two seasons.
9. She and Lena often practice together.
10. Many of Lena's friends have suggested Carrie as a new member of their team.

EXERCISE B   On the line provided, supply a verb that will complete each sentence. In some sentences you will need to include a helping verb.

> **EXAMPLE 1.** For many years the river ___*has flooded*___ every spring.

1. Last month our family _____ Hanukkah, a Jewish religious festival.
2. Hanukkah _____ eight days each year.
3. Rita _____ for Middletown at eight o'clock.
4. She _____ her destination by eleven-thirty tomorrow.
5. The fog _____ us many times on our way to school.
6. I _____ weather like this.
7. Marc _____ his teacher whether he could read a story by Isaac Bashevis Singer.
8. I _____ for a summer job in the spring.
9. I _____ this assignment soon.
10. From now on, I _____ more care with these small jobs.

LANGUAGE HANDBOOK **1** THE PARTS OF SPEECH

WORKSHEET 5 | Identifying Linking and Helping Verbs (Rules 1 f, g)

EXERCISE A   Underline the linking verbs in the following sentences. Be sure to underline any helping verbs as well.

> **EXAMPLE 1.** Jimmy Carter, the thirty-ninth president of the United States, <u>is</u> from Georgia.

1. Atlanta is the capital of Georgia.

2. It has become an important center for trade and manufacturing.

3. The state's forests are a major source of wealth.

4. Lumbering has been an important industry since the early days.

5. Cotton remains one of the most valuable farm products in Georgia.

6. Macon is considered a beautiful old city.

7. This city is the birthplace of Sidney Lanier.

8. Lanier became a well-known poet.

9. Carson McCullers was another native of Georgia.

10. *The Heart Is a Lonely Hunter* is one of her most popular novels.

EXERCISE B   In the following sentences, underline each linking verb once. Underline each helping verb twice. Some linking verbs have helping verbs.

> **EXAMPLE 1.** Gardening <u>remains</u> an important part of many cultures.

1. *Bonsai,* which means "planted in a tray" in Japanese, is the art of growing miniature trees in shallow pots.

2. Bonsai is also the name of a tree that is grown in this manner.

3. A tree will look ancient if the gardener controls its growth.

4. If you prune the tree's roots and branches often, it becomes stunted.

5. The branches are made crooked by tying them with wire.

6. Eventually, the tree will appear twisted and windblown.

7. If you like a tree that smells nice, a pine tree or a cherry tree is a good choice.

8. Your choice of container is important, too.

9. It should be shallow earthenware and can be either plain or glazed.

10. Matsuo Basho's haiku about bonsai, "On a Withered Branch," has become well known.

LANGUAGE HANDBOOK **1** THE PARTS OF SPEECH

WORKSHEET 6 | Identifying and Using Adverbs (Rule 1 h)

EXERCISE A Underline the adverbs in each of the following sentences. Draw two lines under the word each adverb modifies.

> **EXAMPLE 1.** We <u>went</u> <u>back</u> to our books.

1. The temperature of the water at the fish hatchery seldom varies.

2. The water never freezes.

3. It comes from unusually large springs.

4. It is very clear water.

5. Vapor sometimes rises from warm water.

6. Yesterday I read an article on the literature of India.

7. Ancient Indian writers first produced hymns called Vedas in about 1500 B.C.

8. Indian literature then entered its classical period.

9. Writers of this period commonly wrote Sanskrit.

10. Writers still use the classical version of Sanskrit.

EXERCISE B Write a suitable adverb on the line provided within each sentence, and underline the word it modifies. On the line provided at the beginning of the sentence, write the question the adverb answers: *how? when? where?* or *to what extent?*

> **EXAMPLE** ___*how*___ **1.** Nikki and Emilio ___*carefully*___ <u>made</u> plans for their puppet show.

_____ 1. They had _____ wanted to give a puppet show.

_____ 2. The two _____ built a puppet theater and made papier-mâché puppets.

_____ 3. Both _____ painted faces on the puppets.

_____ 4. Nikki and Emilio _____ based their show on a Latin American folk tale about La Llorona.

_____ 5. _____ had they heard of a figure so tragic as the weeping woman.

_____ 6. _____ the day of the show arrived.

_____ 7. They arranged their theater _____ on the lawn.

_____ 8. The show went _____.

_____ 9. The audience applauded _____.

_____ 10. The two performers decided that they would create an even better show _____.

LANGUAGE HANDBOOK **1** **THE PARTS OF SPEECH**

WORSHEET 7 **Identifying Prepositions and Prepositional Phrases (Rule 1 i)**

EXERCISE A Underline each prepositional phrase in the following sentences. Some sentences contain more than one prepositional phrase.

> **EXAMPLE 1.** The discovery of fire was an important event in the history of civilization.

1. Humans' original source of fire was probably lightning.

2. A fire started when a tree was struck by lightning.

3. Early people probably took coals from this fire and preserved them in a shelter.

4. The shelter was often deep within a cave.

5. An attendant may have stayed beside the coals.

6. All fires that the tribe needed probably were started by these coals.

7. If the tribe moved, the keeper of the fire may have carried the coals.

8. Sometimes a small fire was kept burning continuously in the shelter.

9. The attendant probably stayed near the fire and kept it going.

10. Humans first learned how to make their own fire during the Stone Age.

EXERCISE B In the following paragraph, underline each preposition and draw two lines under each object of a preposition.

> **EXAMPLE** [1] Mahatma Gandhi worked to free his country from Britain.

[1] India had been under British rule for many years. [2] Mahatma Gandhi, who was trained as a lawyer, was an Indian reformer and nationalist. [3] Gandhi felt that India would gain freedom only through nonviolent means, so he urged Indians struggling for their independence to boycott British institutions. [4] Because of his religious beliefs, Gandhi believed that the only way an opponent could be conquered was with nonviolence. [5] He believed that violence would bring with it only further violence. [6] His technique of nonviolence was called *satyagraha,* which literally means "grasping for truth." [7] According to Gandhi, anger weakens, but nonviolence is the weapon of the strong. [8] He thought that a country could be administered on a nonviolent basis if the majority of the people were nonviolent. [9] One of the great disappointments of Gandhi's life was that he was not able to make peace between the Hindus and Muslims of his country. [10] He did, however, help India to achieve independence from Great Britain.

| LANGUAGE HANDBOOK | **1** | **THE PARTS OF SPEECH** |

WORKSHEET 8 — Identifying Conjunctions and Interjections; Determining Parts of Speech (Rules 1 j, k)

EXERCISE A   In the following sentences, underline each conjunction once and each interjection twice. Not every sentence has an interjection.

> **EXAMPLE** 1. <u>Wow</u>! The snow <u>and</u> wind are ferocious.

1. Whew! This is certainly a cold and miserable day.

2. It may be cold here, but in Alaska it is even colder.

3. Neither sub-zero temperatures nor deep snow keeps the racers in the Iditarod from packing their sleds and setting out, however.

4. Both the dogs and their drivers often perform well in the cold.

5. Do you want to participate in the race, or do you only want to watch?

6. Hey, we should hurry to find a place at the starting line, for the race is about to begin.

7. The key to winning the Iditarod is not only speed, but also endurance.

8. I enjoy watching the race, yet I don't like standing in the cold.

9. Libby Riddles was exhausted but excited when she became the first woman to win the Iditarod.

10. Gosh, I'm glad I don't have to qualify for and compete in that race!

EXERCISE B   On the line provided, identify the part of speech of each italicized word. Write *N* for noun, *PRON* for pronoun, *ADJ* for adjective, *V* for verb, *ADV* for adverb, *PREP* for preposition, *CONJ* for conjunction, or *INT* for interjection.

> **EXAMPLES** __N__ 1. Tara Lipinski's *dream* was to be an ice skater.
>
> __V__ 2. Do you *dream* of being a famous athlete?

_____ 1. Chief Joseph pleaded the case of the Nez Perce *well*.

_____ 2. *Well,* he was a great leader.

_____ 3. We explored the *river* road.

_____ 4. The *river* is almost overflowing its banks.

_____ 5. Isabel *towers* over the other lacrosse players.

_____ 6. Bright flags flew atop the *towers* of the castle.

_____ 7. We waited a long time *for* Miles.

_____ 8. We didn't complain, *for* we knew he was busy.

_____ 9. Greeting us warmly, Ron said, "Please have *some* refreshments."

_____ 10. *Some* don't care for tuna.

LANGUAGE HANDBOOK **1** THE PARTS OF SPEECH

WORKSHEET 9 | Test (Rules 1 a–k)

EXERCISE A   In the following sentences, underline each noun once and each verb, including helping verbs, twice.

> EXAMPLE 1. The <u>name</u> of the <u>praying mantis</u> <u>comes</u> from the prayerful <u>attitude</u> of its front <u>legs</u>.

1. The mantis is an unusual insect of strange habits.

2. This creature lives in many parts of the world.

3. Perhaps twenty different species can be found in the United States.

4. The mantis is a friend of the farmer.

5. Its victims often include grasshoppers and caterpillars.

6. During its patient wait for prey, the mantis rests motionless on its hind legs.

7. With its strong front legs, it captures insects.

8. The mantis does not injure plants.

9. The praying mantis is used in greenhouses for insect control.

10. A praying mantis may grow to five inches in length.

EXERCISE B   Underline each pronoun in the following sentences.

> EXAMPLE 1. Will <u>you</u> be coming to the play with <u>us</u>?

1. These are our tickets for *Romeo and Juliet*.

2. I think my aunt would like to sit with us, if that is all right with you.

3. She wants to see her son play the part of Mercutio, who is the best friend of Romeo.

4. Your friend Mike designed most of the stage set himself, and he is very proud of it.

5. Do any of you know who wrote *Romeo and Juliet*?

6. His name was William Shakespeare, and he is the author of many of the most famous plays in English literature.

7. In the first act of the play, Romeo cannot keep himself from falling in love with Juliet, whose face he sees from across the room at a party.

8. The ending of the story is very sad, but we decided that we would not reveal it to anyone who had not seen the play.

9. It was the first Shakepeare play that some of us had ever seen.

10. Even though some of the language in the play was difficult for her to follow, my younger sister Sarah surprised herself by crying at the end of it.

Continued ☞

EXERCISE C In the following sentences, underline each adjective once and each adverb twice. Do not underline the articles *a*, *an*, and *the*.

> **EXAMPLE 1.** The <u>ancient</u> Greeks were <u><u>extremely</u></u> <u>superstitious</u> about the mantis.

1. The early Greeks readily believed that mantises had supernatural powers.

2. The mantis is a long, predatory insect.

3. The female mantis lays many eggs in a frothy mass.

4. This mass hardens eventually into an egg case, which is fastened tightly to the woody stem of a plant.

5. The tall milkweed is a very common place to find egg cases.

6. The baby insects soon make small holes in the case and rapidly come out.

7. The newborn mantises often eat each other immediately.

8. The adult mantis is a fierce predator.

9. There are several European varieties of mantis, as well as many North American mantises.

10. These mantises include the Chinese mantis, the largest mantis in North America.

EXERCISE D In the following sentences, underline each prepositional phrase and circle the preposition.

> **EXAMPLE 1.** My mother and her brother are standing (beside) each other (in) the old photograph.

1. Chai went to the library and borrowed several books about horses.

2. The novel *Beloved* by Toni Morrison is about the legacy of slavery.

3. We drove the interstate highway all the way across the country.

4. Along the way, we visited the birthplace of Herbert Hoover in West Branch, Iowa.

5. You can find the dishwashing soap beneath the sink and behind the cleanser.

6. According to the newspaper, the new statue will stand beside the river.

7. Because of the heavy rains and flooding, the bus could not make it through the city.

8. Please park the trailer in front of the house.

9. Did you remember to place the scarecrow near the garden?

10. Ang Lee is known for his excellent films, among them *Sense and Sensibility*.

Continued ☞

EXERCISE E   In the following sentences, underline each conjunction once and each interjection twice. Not every sentence has an interjection.

> EXAMPLE **1.** <u>Hey</u>, is that light along the horizon an airplane, <u>or</u> is it a UFO?

1. Gosh, it's not blinking, and it does not seem to move like an airplane.

2. People either believe in UFOs or they do not.

3. Well, my friends Todd and Louisa believe in flying saucers, yet there is not much evidence that they exist.

4. I thought the light was coming closer, but that was just my imagination.

5. Oops, the light is neither an airplane nor a UFO, but only the planet Venus.

EXERCISE F   On the line provided, identify the part of speech of each italicized word. Write *N* for noun, *PRON* for pronoun, *ADJ* for adjective, *V* for verb, *ADV* for adverb, *PREP* for preposition, *CONJ* for conjunction, or *INT* for interjection.

> EXAMPLE ___PREP___ **1.** Have you heard *of* Lewis and Clark?

_____ **1.** President Jefferson sent Lewis and Clark *across* the continent.

_____ **2.** Their task was to find out the extent and *nature* of the vast territory west of the Mississippi.

_____ **3.** At first, the men *followed* the Missouri River.

_____ **4.** *They* traveled by keelboats and canoes.

_____ **5.** During the *first* winter, they stayed at a Mandan village.

_____ **6.** In April of 1805, they started out *with* a remarkable interpreter.

_____ **7.** She was an American Indian *woman* whose name was Sacajawea, and she carried her infant son on her back.

_____ **8.** She led the explorers across the Great Divide, *and* still they traveled westward.

_____ **9.** *Amazingly,* Sacajawea met her long-lost brother on the expedition.

_____ **10.** When they reached the mouth of the Columbia, Clark wrote in his diary, "*Oh!* the joy!"

LANGUAGE HANDBOOK 2 AGREEMENT

WORKSHEET 1 Using Singular and Plural Forms (Rule 2 a)

EXERCISE A Indicate on the line provided whether each word is singular or plural by writing *S* for singular or *P* for plural.

EXAMPLES ___*S*___ **1.** book

___*P*___ **2.** books

_____ **1.** oxen	_____ **14.** lamps
_____ **2.** mountains	_____ **15.** children
_____ **3.** it	_____ **16.** mice
_____ **4.** topcoat	_____ **17.** chair
_____ **5.** women	_____ **18.** I
_____ **6.** breakfast	_____ **19.** mother-in-law
_____ **7.** intelligence	_____ **20.** assignment
_____ **8.** beaches	_____ **21.** carriages
_____ **9.** we	_____ **22.** nation
_____ **10.** babies	_____ **23.** families
_____ **11.** they	_____ **24.** baseballs
_____ **12.** she	_____ **25.** tickets
_____ **13.** cupfuls	

EXERCISE B Change the words below from singular to plural or from plural to singular. If a word is singular, write the plural form on the line provided. If it is plural, write the singular form. If a word is the same in both its singular and plural forms, write it without change.

EXAMPLE **1.** person _____*persons*_____

1. bottle _____	**6.** we _____
2. sheep _____	**7.** noises _____
3. goat _____	**8.** adenoid _____
4. apples _____	**9.** galaxies _____
5. team _____	**10.** mountain lion _____

LANGUAGE HANDBOOK 2 AGREEMENT

WORKSHEET 2 | **Making Subjects and Verbs Agree (Rules 2 b, d)**

EXERCISE A   Underline the subject of each sentence and the italicized verb in parentheses that agrees with the subject.

> **EXAMPLE** **1.** Jordan's <u>painting</u> (*was*, *were*) extremely well done.

1. My sisters never (*enjoys*, *enjoy*) arguing any more.

2. Your friends (*has*, *have*) gone home by now.

3. The club members (*is*, *are*) planning an overnight hike.

4. You (*turns*, *turn*) left at the first stoplight.

5. The mail carrier (*delivers*, *deliver*) the mail about noon.

6. The breeze (*seems*, *seem*) cooler this evening.

7. Some people really (*does*, *do*) live in glass houses.

8. A baby robin (*eats*, *eat*) its weight in worms every day.

9. We (*was*, *were*) driving to Trout Lake last week.

10. They (*calls*, *call*) two pheasants a "brace."

EXERCISE B   Underline the subject of each sentence and the italicized verb in parentheses that agrees with the subject.

> **EXAMPLE** **1.** The <u>books</u> (*was*, <u>*were*</u>) found in an old trunk.

1. My work (*consists*, *consist*) mainly of outdoor chores.

2. No, it just (*doesn't*, *don't*) seem right to me.

3. No one but Jacqueline (*wants*, *want*) to go.

4. The tomatoes (*has*, *have*) been doing especially well this year.

5. The garden (*doesn't*, *don't*) take as much work as I expected.

6. As I recall, you (*wasn't*, *weren't*) out for the team last year.

7. Some newspapers (*doesn't*, *don't*) print much foreign news.

8. My uncle (*comes*, *come*) to visit us every spring.

9. My grandparents (*was*, *were*) both born in 1931.

10. Morning glories (*closes*, *close*) up their flowers at night.

| WORSHEET 3 | # Using Subjects and Verbs with Prepositional Phrases (Rule 2 c) |

EXERCISE A   Circle the prepositional phrases in the following sentences. Then, underline the subject in each sentence and the verb in parentheses that agrees with the subject.

> **EXAMPLE 1.** The <u>poems</u> (in our literature book) (*is*, <u>*are*</u>) well chosen.

1. The descriptions in the poem about Paul Revere almost (*makes, make*) you forget where you are.

2. Many lines in the poem (*is, are*) especially good.

3. The tramp of feet (*is, are*) heard.

4. The hurrying hoofbeats of Paul Revere's horse (*shatters, shatter*) the silence.

5. The scenes on each village street (*lives, live*) again.

6. Many poems by Longfellow (*has, have*) effective descriptive passages.

7. One of my favorite poems (*is, are*) Lewis Carroll's "Father William."

8. The antics of the old man always (*makes, make*) me laugh.

9. Some of the father's answers to his son (*is, are*) particularly amusing.

10. The father's reason for doing headstands (*tickles, tickle*) my funny bone.

EXERCISE B   In the following paragraph, underline the correct form of the italicized verbs in parentheses.

> **EXAMPLE** The Roman god of travel [1] (<u>*was*</u>, *were*) Mercury.

Of all the planets, Mercury [1] (*is, are*) nearest the sun. The orbit of Mercury [2] (*put, puts*) it within 28,600,000 miles of the sun. Mercury, because of its small orbit, [3] (*move, moves*) faster around the sun than any other planet does. The planet, according to ancient myths, [4] (*was, were*) named after the messenger of the Roman gods. This messenger of theirs [5] (*was, were*) considered to be very fast. Art and stories about him [6] (*describes, describe*) him as wearing winged sandals. At 59 days, Mercury's rotation on its axis [7] (*take, takes*) much longer than Earth's, but the length of Mercury's year [8] (*is, are*) much shorter than Earth's. The planet nearest the sun [9] (*complete, completes*) its orbit in only 88 days. If people live on Mercury, their concept of time surely [10] (*seem, seems*) different from ours.

WORSHEET 4 Ensuring Agreement with Indefinite Pronouns (Rules 2 d–f)

EXERCISE A Underline the verb in parentheses that agrees with its subject in each of the following sentences.

> **EXAMPLE 1.** Everybody on the field trip (*know,* *knows*) not to get close to the bears.

1. Anybody who is interested in boats (*needs, need*) to know how to swim.

2. Everyone in Ms. Gobel's classes (*like, likes*) her.

3. Most of the students (*prefers, prefer*) to go to Paris.

4. Some of these shirts (*costs, cost*) eighteen dollars.

5. Several in the eighth grade (*wants, want*) to have a class picnic in the spring.

6. Everyone in this group (*has, have*) a very definite preference.

7. Both of the maples in our front yard (*turns, turn*) red in the fall.

8. Some of the sky (*becomes, become*) lighter at dawn.

9. Neither of my grandmothers (*has, have*) retired.

10. Few of the documents (*was, were*) authentic.

EXERCISE B Some of the following sentences contain errors in agreement between the subject and the verb. If the italicized verb is incorrect, cross it out and write the correct verb on the line provided. If the sentence is already correct, write *C*.

> **EXAMPLE** __was__ **1.** One of our visits ~~were~~ to the planetarium.

_____ 1. Many of us *has* been fascinated by the wonders of outer space.

_____ 2. Some in our class *is* looking toward the unknown with expectation.

_____ 3. Not one of our astronomers *know* whether life exists on planets in other solar systems.

_____ 4. None of the astronomers *is* sure whether we will encounter hospitable environments on other worlds.

_____ 5. Not everyone *want* to explore the unknown.

_____ 6. Several among us *fears* that alien life forms may be hostile.

_____ 7. A few of us *dream* of being among the first explorers of another planet.

_____ 8. *Does* any of you ever read a science fiction story?

_____ 9. Many of the authors *fills* the universe with unusual creatures.

_____ 10. Among science fiction writers, some *has* made predictions that have come true.

LANGUAGE HANDBOOK 2 AGREEMENT

WORKSHEET 5 — **Ensuring Agreement with Subjects Joined by *And, Or,* or *Nor* (Rules 2 g, h)**

EXERCISE A   In the following sentences, underline each subject and then underline the verb form in parentheses that agrees with the subject.

> **EXAMPLES** 1. <u>Juanita</u> and <u>Chris</u> (*is*, <u>*are*</u>) studying for the math exam.
>
> 2. <u>Rhythm and blues</u> (<u>*is*</u>, *are*) a classic form of American music.

1. LaTonya and Maria (*play*, *plays*) volleyball with John and Conner.

2. Plot and character (*are*, *is*) important elements in a short story.

3. Mosses and lichens (*grow*, *grows*) in the arctic tundra.

4. The president and owner of the software company (*is*, *are*) Elise Washington.

5. Apples, oranges, and bananas (*makes*, *make*) a tasty fruit salad.

6. Country and western (*has*, *have*) many fans.

7. *Little Women* and *Little Men* (*were*, *was*) written by Louisa May Alcott.

8. Macaroni and cheese (*is*, *are*) Nick's favorite meal.

9. Macaroni and cheese (*is*, *are*) the basic ingredients.

10. Sweet-and-sour pork (*was*, *were*) the featured item on the menu.

EXERCISE B   In the following sentences, underline each subject and then underline the verb form in parentheses that agrees with the subject.

> **EXAMPLES** 1. Either <u>Andy</u> or <u>Karla</u> (<u>*has*</u>, *have*) the information you need.
>
> 2. Neither the <u>principal</u> nor the <u>teacher</u> (<u>*was*</u>, *were*) delayed by the snowstorm.

1. Neither Li nor Pang (*read*, *reads*) much science fiction.

2. Neither the committee members nor the chairperson (*was*, *were*) on time.

3. Turquoise jewelry or woven baskets (*is*, *are*) sold at almost every corner in town.

4. (*Are*, *Is*) Jupiter or Zeus the supreme Roman deity?

5. Either the teacher or the students (*reads*, *read*) the directions.

6. Neither Tina nor Fernando (*like*, *likes*) jazz.

7. Channel 7 or Channel 18 (*show*, *shows*) wildlife documentaries.

8. Ms. Galinsky or Mr. Deneuve (*have*, *has*) the details about the meeting.

9. Neither Easter Island nor the Aleutian Islands (*is*, *are*) located in the Atlantic.

10. Neither downhill skiing nor cross-country skiing (*appeals*, *appeal*) to me.

WORKSHEET 6 | **Ensuring Agreement with Collective Nouns and with *Don't* and *Doesn't* (Rules 2 i, k)**

EXERCISE A   In each of the following sentences, underline the verb form in parentheses that agrees with the subject.

> **EXAMPLE 1.** The team (*was*, *were*) happy about winning.

1. A fleet of British ships (*are, is*) sailing into the harbor.

2. The band (*is, are*) playing Irish music tonight.

3. The band (*are, is*) tuning their instruments first.

4. What (*has, have*) the class done to improve their scores?

5. Our family (*talks, talk*) all at once when the discussions get lively.

6. In the stadium, the crowd (*cheer, cheers*) wildly.

7. The Environmental Science Club (*have, has*) started a recycling program.

8. The committee (*check, checks*) their calendars for possible open dates.

9. Who (*are, is*) the staff who disagreed about the new proposal?

10. The staff (*is, are*) in charge of greeting guests.

EXERCISE B   In each of the following sentences, underline the correct contraction in parentheses.

> **EXAMPLE 1.** Cactuses (*doesn't*, *don't*) need much water.

1. Sergei (*don't, doesn't*) remember that Juno is a Roman goddess.

2. Fortunately, my dogs (*doesn't, don't*) bark all night.

3. (*Don't, Doesn't*) the Portuguese language sound beautiful?

4. Marta (*doesn't, don't*) play the oboe as well as she plays the flute.

5. The team members (*don't, doesn't*) run during every practice.

6. My grandmother (*don't, doesn't*) check her e-mail on weekends.

7. (*Doesn't, Don't*) the rainfall sound soothing?

8. You (*don't, doesn't*) have to memorize the formula.

9. Those students (*don't, doesn't*) want the class to end.

10. He (*doesn't, don't*) hear the phone ringing.

LANGUAGE HANDBOOK 2 AGREEMENT

WORKSHEET 7 — Ensuring Agreement in Questions and in Sentences That Begin with *There* and *Here* (Rule 2 j)

EXERCISE Underline the verb in parentheses that agrees with the subject in each of the following sentences. Then, underline the subject.

EXAMPLES 1. (*Does*, *Do*) your father like picnics?

2. There (*is*, *are*) the soccer equipment.

1. Here (*comes*, *come*) the baton twirlers.

2. There (*is*, *are*) twenty students in my French class.

3. (*Do*, *Does*) the members of the team practice?

4. Where (*does*, *do*) Miss Bannerman post the daily bulletin?

5. Here (*is*, *are*) the references you need for your history paper.

6. (*Does*, *Do*) Ms. Chang give many A's?

7. There (*is*, *are*) no ice-skating on the pond unless the flag is up.

8. There (*is*, *are*) many varieties of oak trees.

9. (*Has*, *Have*) Amy asked anyone to the dance?

10. Where (*was*, *were*) the receiver when he passed the ball?

11. (*Do*, *Does*) everyone here like spaghetti?

12. Here (*is*, *are*) the list of students who signed up to work on the play.

13. There (*is*, *are*) many mistakes in your homework, Pam.

14. Here (*is*, *are*) the delivery truck with all the furniture you ordered.

15. (*Isn't*, *Aren't*) the Drama Club rehearsing in the auditorium?

16. Where (*is*, *are*) Stephen with the new uniforms?

17. There (*is*, *are*) a new family on our block.

18. (*Do*, *Does*) Emily Jones have a big dog?

19. There (*is*, *are*) many potholes in the street.

20. (*Has*, *Have*) the names of the winners been announced?

21. (*Don't*, *Doesn't*) attendance matter to you?

22. (*Hasn't*, *Haven't*) Andres passed his driving test?

23. Where (*is*, *are*) one of those sprayers for watering plants?

24. (*Was*, *Were*) the boys going to cook dinner for the girls?

25. Here (*is*, *are*) several of the books you wanted.

WORKSHEET 8 — Ensuring Agreement with Singular Words That Have Plural Forms (Rules 2 l–n)

EXERCISE   In each of the following sentences, underline the verb form in parentheses that agrees with the subject.

> **EXAMPLE 1.** Twelve inches (*is*, *are*) equivalent to one foot.

1. The evening news (*come*, *comes*) on right after *Jeopardy!*

2. "The First Americans" (*is*, *are*) a persuasive speech about the inaccurate portrayal of American Indians in some textbooks.

3. Thirty-seven dollars (*are*, *is*) too much to pay for that T-shirt.

4. Physics (*describes*, *describe*) the physical properties and composition of matter and energy.

5. The United Nations (*meet*, *meets*) in New York City.

6. A fortnight (*are*, *is*) two weeks.

7. Four cups of flour (*is*, *are*) about right for this recipe.

8. Measles (*cause*, *causes*) spots to break out on a person's skin.

9. *The Birds* (*is*, *are*) a film by Alfred Hitchcock.

10. Civics (*are*, *is*) a school subject dealing with the rights and duties of citizens.

11. "The Dogs Could Teach Me" (*is*, *are*) a story told from the first-person point of view.

12. Twenty pounds (*feel*, *feels*) quite heavy.

13. One hundred kilometers (*are*, *is*) not as far as one hundred miles.

14. Proverbs (*is*, *are*) a book in the Bible.

15. Genetics (*helps*, *help*) explain the variations of living things.

16. First Choice Motors (*offer*, *offers*) superior service to their customers.

17. The United Arab Emirates (*are*, *is*) a country composed of seven sheikdoms.

18. Fifteen minutes (*equals*, *equal*) a quarter-hour.

19. The Netherlands (*includes*, *include*) the region of Holland.

20. Electronics (*are*, *is*) a branch of physics that deals with electrons and electronic devices.

21. Five minutes (*seems*, *seem*) like a long time to young children.

22. Economics (*is*, *are*) a social science concerned with goods and services.

23. The United States (*contain*, *contains*) fifty states.

24. Fifty dollars (*was*, *were*) all we needed.

25. Four quarts (*make*, *makes*) a gallon.

NAME _____ CLASS _____ DATE _____

LANGUAGE HANDBOOK **2** AGREEMENT

WORKSHEET 9 Ensuring Agreement Between Pronoun and Antecedent (Rules 2 o–s)

EXERCISE On the line provided in each of the following sentences, write a pronoun or a pair of pronouns that agrees with the antecedent or antecedents. Underline the antecedent or antecedents.

EXAMPLES 1. Not <u>one</u> of the students lost __*his or her*__ book.
2. <u>Brad</u> and <u>Sylvia</u> practiced ___*their*___ lines.

1. Dawna said _____ liked the musical play *Fiddler on the Roof.*

2. Both Ramone and Ignacio presented _____ reports on Thailand.

3. Our dog Buster wags _____ tail whenever we enter the room.

4. Edgar Allan Poe was known for _____ horror stories.

5. Everyone brought _____ notebook to class today.

6. My social studies book has a stain on _____ front cover.

7. Irwin Shapiro's interest in American folklore led _____ to a career in writing.

8. My dad said _____ enjoyed reading "Davy Is Born" by Irwin Shapiro.

9. Many of the students in my class said _____ enjoyed the story, too.

10. No one remembered to develop _____ photos of Enchanted Rock.

11. You can't have _____ friends over until the dishes are done.

12. Paula hopes _____ track shoes are in her sports bag.

13. Janet said _____ and the other girls would be in the playoffs.

14. Virginia Driving Hawk Sneve writes about _____ Sioux heritage.

15. Any of you may call _____ parents for permission to stay later.

16. I lent _____ programmable calculator to Iris.

17. The rabbit dashed into _____ burrow.

18. The hikers quenched _____ thirst with water.

19. Writer Amy Ling was born in China but moved with _____ family to the United States.

20. Each of the boys brought _____ parents to the meeting.

21. Shel Silverstein is best known for _____ poems and drawings for children.

22. Several of the students shared _____ poems with the class.

23. Each of the players signed _____ name to the petition.

24. Does a frightened ostrich really hide _____ head in the sand?

25. In *The Incredible Journey,* two dogs and a cat find _____ way back home.

20 *Language Handbook Worksheets* *Elements of Literature*

LANGUAGE **2** **AGREEMENT**
HANDBOOK

WORKSHEET 10 | **Avoiding Problems in Agreement of Pronoun and Antecedent (Rules 2 p–r)**

EXERCISE On the line provided in each of the following sentences, write a pronoun or a pair of pronouns that agrees with the antecedent. Underline the antecedent.

> EXAMPLES 1. <u>Each</u> of the committee members can read ___*his or her*___ report.
>
> 2. <u>Several</u> of the students volunteered ____*their*____ time.

1. All of the trees dropped _____ leaves.

2. Neither Andrea nor Estella turned in _____ homework.

3. Most of the students read _____ favorite novels instead.

4. Everybody is waiting for _____ turn.

5. Anyone bringing in _____ food donation is encouraged to do so early.

6. Several of the people eagerly shared _____ experiences of a visit to the Zuni Pueblo in New Mexico.

7. Nobody, however, brought _____ souvenirs to show the others.

8. Each of the girls took _____ own tent to the camp out.

9. Someone named Roy dropped _____ homework in the hall.

10. Everyone recited _____ favorite lines from Dr. Seuss.

11. Most of the bees had returned to _____ hive.

12. A few of the band students forgot to bring _____ sheet music.

13. Has somebody lost _____ book bag?

14. If you find either of my brothers at the park, please tell _____ to come home.

15. Many of these African folk tales are noted for _____ animal characters.

16. Have any of the kittens opened _____ eyes yet?

17. No one can take _____ project home until after it has been graded.

18. Is there anybody who can lend _____ book to Graciella for a few minutes?

19. Some of the paintings revealed _____ creators' love of nature.

20. None of the artist's work had lost _____ appeal to modern audiences.

21. Both of the pianists said _____ favorite composer was Chopin.

22. Most of the food had lost _____ freshness.

23. One of the girls decided to write _____ report on the Apache chief Geronimo.

24. None of the peacocks spread _____ tail feathers.

25. Neither of the dogs wagged _____ tail when we returned.

WORKSHEET 11   Ensuring Pronoun-Antecedent Agreement with *And, Or,* and *Nor* (Rules 2 s, t)

EXERCISE A   On the line provided in each sentence, write a pronoun that agrees with its antecedent or antecedents.

> **EXAMPLES** 1. Both Debra and Stephanie invited ____*their*____ parents.
>
> 2. Do you know if Joseph or Conrad will bring ____*his*____ guitar to the hayride?

1. Neither Julian nor Kevin memorized _____ speech.

2. Both Carla and Annie wanted _____ own bikes.

3. Heidi and Sara spent _____ allowances on birthday gifts.

4. Marie or Tonya will bring _____ CD player to the party.

5. John and Bryan took _____ dogs to the park.

6. Wendy or Karen will read _____ poem to the seminar.

7. Both the new bicycle and the new car got _____ first dents on the same day.

8. Phil, Leon, or Mario will bring _____ parents.

9. The tractor and the flatbed wagon had mud all over _____ wheels.

10. Neither Nikki nor Jacqui forgets to wear _____ seat belt in the car.

11. Will the Senate or the House pass _____ version of the bill first?

12. Both the senator and the representative from our district have said _____ will support the President's position.

13. I wish I could remember whether the Thai restaurant or the Mexican restaurant was providing _____ services for my brother's wedding.

14. Was it Todd, Martin, or Sylvester who told you that _____ would lend you his tennis racket?

15. Sybil, Gordon, and Ms. Tanaka all said that _____ would contribute.

16. After submitting a story to the anthology, neither Leo, Glen, nor Jim was certain that _____ story would be accepted.

17. As they watched oil leaking from the crankcase, both Steve and Judy knew that _____ concern for the car was justified.

18. Before they all came to class, I wondered if Brad, his father, or Mr. Gee would remember to bring _____ notebook.

19. Before Martin and Julia got married, _____ asked the minister to hold the ceremony in the morning.

20. Every time Joan Sutherland or Maria Callas sang, _____ held the audience spellbound.

Continued ☞

LANGUAGE HANDBOOK 2 WORKSHEET 11 *(continued)*

EXERCISE B On the lines provided, rewrite each of the following sentences to avoid joining singular and plural antecedents or antecedents of different genders.

EXAMPLES 1. Neither Mr. Marks nor the Talbots will be taking their car to the movies. *Mr. Marks will not be taking his car to the movies, nor will the Talbots be taking theirs.*

2. Either Iola or Chuck will give the teacher her or his assignment first. *Either Iola will give the teacher her assigment first, or Chuck will give the teacher his.*

1. Either Jennifer or Walter will be bringing her or his catcher's mitt to the softball game.

_____

_____

_____

_____

2. Either Joseph or the Wongs will surprise us with their special recipe at the dinner party. _____

_____

_____

_____

3. Neither Christopher nor Louise submitted his or her story to the student newspaper.

_____

_____

_____

4. I suppose that neither Clancy nor the Donovans will be willing to give us their account of what happened. _____

_____

_____

_____

LANGUAGE HANDBOOK **2** **AGREEMENT**

WORSHEET 12 **Avoiding Problems in Agreement of Pronoun and Antecedent (Rules 2 u–w)**

EXERCISE On the line provided in each of the following sentences, write a pronoun or a pair of pronouns that agrees with its antecedent. Underline the antecedent.

EXAMPLES 1. The <u>audience</u> clapped ___their___ hands.

2. There is no cure for <u>mumps</u>, but there is a vaccine against ___it___.

3. When I paid only <u>six dollars</u>, ___it___ was less than I expected.

1. The swarm of bees flew to _____ hive.

2. Stan biked the two miles to school today, but usually he walks _____.

3. Has the committee on foreign relations presented _____ report yet?

4. The news wasn't very interesting, but _____ was accurate.

5. The group usually bring _____ suggestions to the monthly meetings.

6. The family is taking _____ vacation next month.

7. Congress may vote according to _____ convictions.

8. The flock of ducks made _____ way south for the winter.

9. The two quarts of milk filled _____ container to the brim.

10. The English poet Alfred, Lord Tennyson wrote *Idylls of the King,* famous for _____ portrayal of Merlin, King Arthur, and the knights of the Round Table.

11. Were the herd of goats enjoying _____ feast of old tin cans?

12. The jury finally reached _____ decision.

13. They had sixty-three cents, but _____ was not enough.

14. The assembly cast _____ votes to elect Gabriel Ortiz as president.

15. Physics is challenging, but _____ is also fascinating.

16. We bought ten pounds of potatoes, and _____ was too much.

17. We studied civics, and _____ was a difficult subject.

18. The public voiced _____ opinions about building the World Cultures Institute.

19. The committee could not agree on _____ plan of action.

20. Measles is generally a childhood disease, but _____ can afflict adults as well.

21. Did the Italian soccer team lose _____ first game?

22. The orchestra tuned _____ instruments before the concert.

23. The yearbook staff have turned in _____ suggestions for this year's title.

24. Ten miles is not a long way to bicycle, but _____ is far for most people to run.

25. The class has chosen _____ leader.

LANGUAGE HANDBOOK **2** AGREEMENT

WORKSHEET 13 | Test (Rules 2 a–w)

EXERCISE A   On the line provided, indicate whether each word is singular or plural by writing *S* for singular or *P* for plural.

EXAMPLES   __*S*__   **1.** tooth

__*P*__   **2.** feet

_____ **1.** football   _____ **6.** pocket

_____ **2.** statues   _____ **7.** government

_____ **3.** us   _____ **8.** stories

_____ **4.** tool   _____ **9.** stoplights

_____ **5.** brothers-in-law   _____ **10.** navy

EXERCISE B   Underline the correct italicized word in parentheses.

EXAMPLES   **1.** Both writers (*is*, *are*) well known.

2. (*Doesn't*, *Don't*) James or Raul have a power drill?

1. (*There's*, *There are*) few potential leaders in this group.

2. Either Theo or Jerry (*is*, *are*) destined to be Ed's successor.

3. Why (*doesn't*, *don't*) he ever come along with us?

4. There (*is*, *are*) some students who are more interested in writing than others.

5. Neither Ms. Columbo nor Mr. Andrews (*was*, *were*) able to tell where the trouble lay.

6. Their plan for the festivities (*was*, *were*) very well thought out.

7. Each of the contestants (*seems*, *seem*) well qualified for the scholarship.

8. Both of the students (*hopes*, *hope*) to win the essay contest.

9. One of those drugstores (*has*, *have*) a big sale this week.

10. I (*doesn't*, *don't*) know where I left my tennis racket.

11. The other players (*don't*, *doesn't*) know where it is, either.

12. (*Does*, *Do*) the pen and pencil come as a set?

13. None of these stores (*sells*, *sell*) the kinds of shoes I want.

14. At 2:00 P.M., the soccer team (*board*, *boards*) the bus to the away game.

15. The team (*retrieve*, *retrieves*) their equipment from the locker room.

16. We (*was*, *were*) talking about these machines in French class.

17. One of the articles (*is*, *are*) about the letters of Abigail Adams.

Continued ☞

18. Here (*comes, come*) Mom and Dad now.

19. You (*wasn't, weren't*) home when we telephoned.

20. There (*isn't, aren't*) any letters in the mailbox.

EXERCISE C   Circle the subject in each of the following sentences. If there is an agreement error, draw a line through the incorrect verb and write the correct form on the line provided. If the sentence is already correct, write *C*.

EXAMPLES ___C___ **1.** (One) of these books is about the sea.

___has___ **2.** (Neither) of the girls ~~have~~ the information.

_____ **1.** The effects of the long dry spell was disastrous for crops and cattle.

_____ **2.** There was too many swimmers at the pool.

_____ **3.** Here is two recipes for bread without any salt.

_____ **4.** There is beauty in every facet of nature.

_____ **5.** Each of these books have some good descriptions.

_____ **6.** Towns and seaports were springing up.

_____ **7.** A wild tale of hidden riches were enough to start a bold expedition.

_____ **8.** One of the most daring mountain climbers was Annie Peck.

_____ **9.** Early explorations or pioneer adventures offer many topics for reports.

_____ **10.** Trade with other countries are important for our prosperity.

EXERCISE D   In each of the following sentences, circle the subject and underline the correct verb form in parentheses.

EXAMPLES **1.** (Some) of the speeches (*was, __were__*) too long.

2. (Abbott and Costello) (*is, __are__*) still very funny.

1. None of the snakes (*has, have*) shed this early in the season.

2. The Lions Club (*meets, meet*) every Tuesday.

3. Lola and Sam (*plan, plans*) to study Russian next year.

4. Twenty pounds (*are, is*) about how much my dog weighs.

5. Mathematics (*is, are*) Derek's favorite subject.

6. The writer and director of the play (*were, was*) Ms. Goldfarb.

7. Most of the meal (*was, were*) left untouched.

8. Two-and-a-half months (*is, are*) long enough for our summer vacation.

Continued ☞

9. "Points of View" (*are, is*) the title of a poem by Ishmael Reed.

10. The news tonight (*are, is*) mostly about the floods in Texas.

EXERCISE E   Underline the verb in parentheses that agrees with the subject.

> **EXAMPLE**   **1.** Either John or Debra (*know, <u>knows</u>*) where the meeting is.

1. Either Carmen or her brother (*has, have*) offered to have the meeting at their house.

2. They and the Bellinis (*lives, live*) across the street from the school.

3. Kelly and another committee member (*has, have*) already arrived.

4. Neither Al nor his brothers (*is, are*) able to be here.

5. Either the faculty advisors or Carmen (*is, are*) going to conduct the business meeting.

6. Bob or Kelly (*reads, read*) the treasurer's report when Al can't come.

7. (*Does, Do*) Carmen and the other members get bored during the business meeting?

8. The girls and boys (*takes, take*) turns bringing the refreshments.

9. Either a carton of fruit juice or a plate of fruit (*is, are*) in the bag beside the sink.

10. Usually Joe and some of the others (*comes, come*) solely because of the refreshments.

EXERCISE F   On the line provided in each of the following sentences, write a pronoun or a pair of pronouns that agrees with the antecedent. Underline the antecedent.

> **EXAMPLES**   **1.** <u>Julia</u> lent _____*her*_____ guitar to Anne.
>
>   **2.** <u>Dashiell Hammett</u> and <u>Raymond Chandler</u> are known for _____*their*_____ hard-boiled detective novels.

1. Either LaTonya or Darlene will sing _____ song first.

2. After the band and the choir finish rehearsal, _____ will have some refreshments.

3. Only some of the players remembered to bring _____ equipment.

4. The bill was for ten dollars, but _____ was a reasonable amount.

5. The team has practiced for _____ match with Argentina.

6. The animal licked _____ wounded paw.

7. We thought economics might be hard, but _____ wasn't.

8. All of the tomato plants had fruit on _____ vines.

9. Everyone needs to listen to _____ own heart.

10. Before our music class went to hear "Peter and the Wolf" performed live, we listened to a recording of _____.

LANGUAGE HANDBOOK **3** USING VERBS

WORKSHEET 1 Identifying Past, Present, and Future Tenses
(Rules 3 a, b, d)

EXERCISE A   On the lines provided, write the two missing principal parts of each of the following regular verbs. Include the helping verb *have* with the past participle.

	Base Form	Present Participle	Past	Past Participle
EXAMPLE **1.**	use	_using_	used	_(have) used_

	Base Form	Present Participle	Past	Past Participle
1.	_____	believing	believed	_____
2.	shout	shouting	_____	_____
3.	ask	_____	asked	_____
4.	like	liking	_____	_____
5.	_____	_____	climbed	(have) climbed
6.	_____	working	_____	(have) worked
7.	_____	smiling	_____	(have) smiled
8.	follow	_____	followed	_____
9.	_____	_____	supported	(have) supported
10.	_____	completing	_____	(have) completed

EXERCISE B   On the line provided for each sentence, write the correct principal part of the verb in parentheses, depending on the meaning of the sentence.

EXAMPLE _burning_ **1.** The wood in the stove is (*burn*) steadily.

_____ **1.** Our city is (*sponsor*) an energy conservation campaign.

_____ **2.** At school yesterday, we (*listen*) to a speech about how to cut down on the use of fuel.

_____ **3.** Mr. Thompson, the custodian, has (*switch*) the thermostat down.

_____ **4.** Half the light bulbs in the hallways have been (*remove*).

_____ **5.** We are (*switch*) off the lights now.

_____ **6.** My mother has (*change*) the temperature of the water heater to a lower setting.

_____ **7.** We (*close*) the valve of the radiator in the guest room and opened the door.

_____ **8.** People with greenhouses are (*gain*) heat from the trapped sunlight.

_____ **9.** Many citizens are (*purchase*) wood-burning stoves, too.

_____ **10.** I think we have (*achieve*) progress in energy conservation.

LANGUAGE HANDBOOK 3 USING VERBS

WORKSHEET 2 | **Using Irregular Verbs (Rule 3 c)**

EXERCISE On the line provided, write the correct past tense or past participle form of the italicized verb in parentheses. Remember that the past participle must be used with any form of the helping verb *have*.

EXAMPLE ___flew___ 1. My mother (*fly*) to New Mexico for a business meeting.

_____ 1. Paul (*do*) his homework last night.

_____ 2. After Ann had finished her poster, we (*put*) it on the wall.

_____ 3. Have you (*go*) to the library already?

_____ 4. We (*take*) a casserole to the party last night.

_____ 5. I had (*begin*) painting the living room that morning.

_____ 6. Yesterday I (*see*) Ed across the street.

_____ 7. Jacob (*read*) a good book last week.

_____ 8. Have you (*lend*) Maria your bicycle?

_____ 9. Paul has (*make*) a bookcase out of bricks and planks.

_____ 10. We should have (*come*) to the theater earlier.

_____ 11. Gillian (*hurt*) her ankle playing basketball last weekend.

_____ 12. Have you (*break*) my pencil?

_____ 13. Until now, she has not (*teach*) this class at night.

_____ 14. I should have (*keep*) the recipe for banana bread.

_____ 15. This past summer unexpected guests (*eat*) us out of house and home.

_____ 16. My parents had (*find*) some time to go shopping.

_____ 17. This morning we (*drink*) all the juice at breakfast.

_____ 18. We had (*spread*) the blanket on the beach.

_____ 19. After they left, I (*know*) I had to do my English assignment.

_____ 20. The balloon (*burst*) when Tomas stuck it with a pin.

_____ 21. Have you (*send*) her a letter yet?

_____ 22. Aunt Ida (*ring*) the bell and waited.

_____ 23. Ray (*drive*) all the way to Lincoln yesterday.

_____ 24. Hasn't the kitten (*become*) less timid?

_____ 25. The building (*shake*) as the tornado blew past.

LANGUAGE HANDBOOK 3 USING VERBS

WORKSHEET 3 | **More Practice with Irregular Verbs (Rule 3 c)**

EXERCISE A   On the line provided, write the correct past or past participle form of each verb in parentheses. Remember that the past participle must be used with any form of the helping verb *have*.

EXAMPLE ___*seen*___ **1.** Have you (*see*) all of the flocks of geese flying south for the winter?

_____ **1.** Laura, have you (*take*) your tennis racket to be repaired?

_____ **2.** Yesterday Donna (*make*) a special meal for her mother.

_____ **3.** Have you (*shoot*) any pictures yet, Ilona?

_____ **4.** With your help, I have (*find*) my jacket.

_____ **5.** The Tarbelles have (*begin*) to build a cabin next to ours.

_____ **6.** My niece was delighted when she (*hold*) our little kitten.

_____ **7.** Have you (*speak*) to Eva about our picnic?

_____ **8.** Mother has already (*write*) to Aunt Helen.

_____ **9.** Willis, have you (*throw*) away all the old newspapers?

_____ **10.** I (*know*) Sean Callahan when we were in grade school.

_____ **11.** My cousin (*teach*) me to play checkers when I was eight.

_____ **12.** We have (*drive*) on this highway before.

_____ **13.** Have you ever (*fly*) in an airplane?

_____ **14.** Victoria Woodhull (*run*) for president in 1872.

_____ **15.** Yesterday we (*swim*) to the raft in the middle of the lake.

_____ **16.** We (*bring*) our lunch to school today.

_____ **17.** Have you (*choose*) your committee, George?

_____ **18.** We (*drink*) all the lemonade that was waiting for us at the finish line.

_____ **19.** I have (*know*) Mae Wing for several years.

_____ **20.** Who (*throw*) this notebook in the wastebasket?

_____ **21.** The milk has (*freeze*) in the bottles.

_____ **22.** Have you ever (*swim*) across Mirror Lake?

_____ **23.** I would have been on time if I hadn't (*break*) my watch.

_____ **24.** Theresa (*think*) she should take French instead of Spanish.

_____ **25.** They (*begin*) the meeting more than an hour late.

Continued ☞

LANGUAGE HANDBOOK **3** **WORKSHEET 3** *(continued)*

EXERCISE B   Underline the correct italicized verb in parentheses.

> **EXAMPLE** **1.** The mail carrier (*rang*, *rung*) the doorbell twice.

1. That you have (*did, done*) your best is all that matters.

2. We (*have come, come*) a long way to be here tonight.

3. Have they (*saw, seen*) your new guitar yet?

4. Rose Marie and Janice (*gone, went*) shopping.

5. The Sunday newspaper has not (*came, come*) yet.

6. Has he (*did, done*) what he promised to do?

7. The girls on the ball team (*came, come*) early yesterday.

8. We (*seen, saw*) her earlier this morning.

9. Has Roy (*went, gone*) to have his picture taken yet?

10. My aunt and uncle have (*came, come*) for dinner.

EXERCISE C   Draw a line through any italicized verb that is used incorrectly, and write the correct verb form above it. If the italicized verb is already correct, write *C* above it.

> *sang*   *C*
> **EXAMPLE** We [1] ~~sung~~ some songs around the campfire and [2] *told* ghost stories.

As it began to get cooler, I [1] *brung* my sleeping bag closer to the fire and unrolled it. Then I [2] *took* the pail down to the stream and filled it. I [3] *drunk* from the same clear mountain stream in which I had [4] *swam* earlier in the day. Only yesterday, I had [5] *rode* up from the valley with my friend Henry Feather, who has [6] *ran* the outfitting service at Jackson ever since his uncle sold it to him. I felt far away from my everyday life at home. I had come by train as far as Jackson. Then we had [7] *drove* by jeep to the Dugan ranch and had [8] *rode* from there. I [9] *knowed* I would have much to tell my parents when I next [10] *wrote* to them.

LANGUAGE HANDBOOK **3** USING VERBS

WORKSHEET 4 | Identifying and Using Verb Tenses (Rule 3 d)

EXERCISE A   Identify the tense of the italicized verb in each of the following sentences by writing *present, past, future, present perfect, past perfect,* or *future perfect* on the line provided.

EXAMPLE ____*future*____ **1.** Ms. Steinley *will substitute* today.

_____ **1.** They *lived* in Vietnam for ten years before moving to the United States.

_____ **2.** We *will have finished* our work by the time you arrive this afternoon.

_____ **3.** Chester told me that he *has lived* in the same house all his life.

_____ **4.** We *will see* the Eiffel Tower when we go to Paris next summer.

_____ **5.** The Olsons *had built* a new home before selling their old one last year.

_____ **6.** Trisha *entered* her lamb in the county livestock show last spring.

_____ **7.** Dad *loves* growing tomatoes in our back yard every summer.

_____ **8.** We *have researched* our facts for the next debate.

_____ **9.** Daryl *will have gone* to the concert by then.

_____ **10.** The guide *had given* us good information on places to visit.

EXERCISE B   On the lines provided, rewrite each of the following sentences by changing the verb(s) to the tense indicated in parentheses.

EXAMPLE **1.** Sarah planned our trip to the coast. (*future*)
Sarah will plan our trip to the coast.

1. The band has played the same songs at every game. (*present*) _____
_____

2. We saw several whales as we cruised beyond the waters of the bay. (*past perfect*) ____
_____
_____

3. Andrea will demonstrate the proper way to fold the flag. (*past*) _____
_____
_____

Continued ☞

LANGUAGE HANDBOOK **3** **WORKSHEET 4** *(continued)*

4. The butterflies migrate to Mexico by the end of fall. (*future perfect*) _____

_____

_____

5. Mr. Sharp showed us how to block a scene in theater class today. (*present perfect*)

_____

_____

_____

6. The rancher had explained to us the difference between an emu and an ostrich. (*future*)

_____

_____

_____

7. Ahmed will have taken his brother home by now. (*present perfect*) _____

_____

_____

8. Many divers had known about Jacob's Well for years. (*past*) _____

_____

_____

9. We began our tour of British Columbia after visiting Seattle. (*future perfect*) _____

_____

_____

10. The students have handed in their homework. (*past perfect*) _____

_____

_____

_____

LANGUAGE HANDBOOK **3** USING VERBS

WORKSHEET 5 | Using Consistent Verb Tense (Rule 3 e)

EXERCISE A   In the following paragraph, the verb tenses are not consistent. Decide whether the paragraph should be in the present tense or past tense. Then, on the lines provided, rewrite the paragraph, making sure to use consistent verb tense.

EXAMPLE [1] When Jeff invited me to go to the carnival with his family, I say, "Yes."

[1] <u>When Jeff invited me to go to the carnival with his family, I said, "Yes." **or** When Jeff invites me to go to the carnival with his family, I say, "Yes."</u>

[1] By the time Saturday came, I am ready to go. [2] Jeff's parents drive us there, and we parked as close to the front entrance as we can. [3] After making arrangements to meet them in two hours at the bumper cars, we walk down the midway. [4] There were all kinds of rides, and we decide which ones we wanted to try. [5] We found a ticket booth, and we each buy twelve tickets. [6] For the first ride, we take it easy and just went on the Ferris wheel. [7] It's fun to see all the lights when we were stopped at the top of the wheel. [8] After that, we went on a couple of wild rides that are scary but fun. [9] All that excitement makes us thirsty, so we find a refreshment stand and ordered two lemonades. [10] Before we know it, it was ten o'clock and time to meet Jeff's parents.

_____

_____

_____

_____

_____

_____

_____

_____

_____

_____

Continued ☞

LANGUAGE HANDBOOK **3** **WORKSHEET 5** *(continued)*

_____

_____

_____

_____

_____

_____

_____

_____

_____

_____

EXERCISE B   In the following paragraph, the verb tenses are not consistent. Decide whether the paragraph should be in the present tense or past tense. Then, on the lines provided, rewrite the paragraph, making sure to use consistent verb tense.

EXAMPLE   [1] Eleanor Roosevelt is born in 1884 and died in 1962.

[1] Eleanor Roosevelt was born in 1884 and died in 1962. *or*
     Eleanor Roosevelt is born in 1884 and dies in 1962.

[1] Eleanor Roosevelt's parents died when she was nine, so she is raised by her grandmother and sent to school in England. [2] There, she was influenced by headmistress Marie Souvestre, who works for social causes. [3] As a young adult, Eleanor participated in social work before she marries Franklin Delano Roosevelt. [4] After her husband enters politics, she works for the American Red Cross during World War I and later became more involved in politics herself. [5] In the early 1930s, Mrs. Roosevelt becomes a leading activist for women's rights. [6] When her husband was elected President of the United States, Mrs. Roosevelt helps other women get appointed to government positions. [7] She travels around the country, visited coal mines and slums, and speaks out for the poor. [8] After her husband's death, Mrs. Roosevelt is appointed by President Truman to be a delegate to the United Nations, where she supported the UN's Declaration of Human Rights. [9] This service in the UN is probably her greatest achievement. [10] Eleanor Roosevelt devoted herself to the causes of humanity and is loved by many.

Continued ☞

LANGUAGE HANDBOOK **3** USING VERBS

WORKSHEET 6 | **Identifying and Using Active and Passive Voice (Rule 3 f)**

EXERCISE A   On the line provided, identify the verb in each of the following sentences as *AV* for active voice or *PV* for passive voice.

EXAMPLE   ___PV___   **1.** The arctic tundra is characterized by long winters, little snow, and low temperatures.

_____ **1.** Warm summer temperatures thaw the tundra's surface soil but not the subsoil, or permafrost.

_____ **2.** Therefore, water drainage is hindered by flat and partially frozen ground.

_____ **3.** Ponds and bogs, sources of moisture for plants, are formed by standing water.

_____ **4.** Typical arctic vegetation includes low plants, such as cotton grass, sedge, and lichens.

_____ **5.** Soil disturbances such as "flowing soil" are caused by thaws and movement of soil.

_____ **6.** Irregular landforms, such as hummocks, frost boils, and earth stripes, are produced by poorly drained areas.

_____ **7.** On the soft surface, deep gullies are caused by vehicle tracks.

_____ **8.** The disruption of vegetation by vehicles melts permafrost.

_____ **9.** Most arctic vegetation, however, can survive these soil disturbances.

_____ **10.** Arctic wildlife is found on the tundra as well.

EXERCISE B   In the following sentences, first determine whether the sentence is in the active or the passive voice. Then, on the lines provided, rewrite each sentence in the other voice.

EXAMPLES **1.** The tennis ball was served by Sharmaine. _Sharmaine served the tennis ball._

2. My parents praised me for my good attitude. _My good attitude was praised by my parents._

1. Dad cooked a lasagna dinner for the family last night. _____

_____

_____

Continued ☞

2. The folk-dancing class was attended by several members of our foreign cultures club.

_____

_____

3. Sarah invited some friends to go to the movies with her on Saturday. _____

_____

_____

4. Famous works of art in the Louvre Museum in Paris are seen by many people. _____

_____

_____

5. Our pecan tree was pruned by a professional tree trimmer. _____

_____

_____

6. Glen gave a slide show and lecture on native plants of the Southwest. _____

_____

_____

7. Lincoln's Gettysburg Address was read by the students. _____

_____

_____

8. The Hardens invited me to their annual Labor Day picnic. _____

_____

_____

9. Our dog was given his rabies vaccination by Dr. Lambert. _____

_____

_____

10. Our computer was fixed by a technician. _____

_____

_____

LANGUAGE HANDBOOK **3** USING VERBS

WORKSHEET 7 Using *Sit* and *Set*

EXERCISE A Underline the correct verb form in each of the following sentences.

EXAMPLE 1. The cat has been (*sitting*, *setting*) on the roof all day.

1. How long has that child been (*sitting*, *setting*) on the steps?

2. I will (*sit*, *set*) the pan back on the stove.

3. Has this clock been (*sitting*, *setting*) on the mantel all the time?

4. We (*sat*, *set*) with Frank on the bus yesterday morning.

5. Dorothy (*sat*, *set*) her skates on the bench.

6. I have (*sat*, *set*) here for an hour reading this book.

7. We were (*sitting*, *setting*) at our desks when Mr. McGovern came in.

8. We were supposed to (*sit*, *set*) the forks next to the knives.

9. Chris will (*sit*, *set*) up front and listen intently.

10. The mail carrier has (*sat*, *set*) the magazines on the porch chair.

EXERCISE B Write the correct form of *sit* or *set* on each line in the following sentences.

EXAMPLE 1. Please ___set___ the groceries on the counter.

1. How long did you _____ in the chair by the window?

2. Whatever you do, don't _____ that ice sculpture in direct sunlight.

3. The leader of the seminar told the participants to _____ in a circle.

4. She can't come to the phone right now because she is _____ several pies on the windowsill to cool.

5. Mr. Polley always wipes the table clean before he _____ the plates and glasses on it.

6. Whenever she can, Tara _____ in the front row of the auditorium during assembly.

7. Ms. Fournier is especially careful when she is _____ the glass figurines on the shelves of her shop.

8. Children often become restless when they have been _____ for a long time.

9. _____ aside the spices for the curry before you begin chopping the vegetables.

10. Dean always _____ in the back row of the movie theater.

LANGUAGE HANDBOOK 3 USING VERBS

WORKSHEET 8 | Using *Lie* and *Lay*

EXERCISE A Underline the correct verb form in each of the following sentences.

> **EXAMPLE 1.** The lifeguard was (<u>*lying*</u>, *laying*) on the raft.

1. Buster is (*lying*, *laying*) on the mat on the front porch.

2. Jerry, you may (*lie*, *lay*) the blanket on the grass.

3. The children (*lay*, *laid*) on the beach after their swim.

4. I'll (*lie*, *lay*) this green rug in front of my dresser.

5. The rake is (*lying*, *laying*) on the grass in the rain.

6. The other tools have (*lain*, *laid*) in the garage all week.

7. Workers are (*lying*, *laying*) the new linoleum.

8. Alice has (*lain*, *laid*) the book on the librarian's desk.

9. I just (*lay*, *laid*) the paper on the table.

10. You should (*lie*, *lay*) down for a short rest, Pat.

EXERCISE B Write the correct form of *lie* or *lay* on each line in the following sentences.

> **EXAMPLE 1.** Where did you ___*lay*___ the serving spoon?

1. It is _____ right next to the cutting board.

2. My mother often likes to _____ down on the couch for half an hour after work.

3. While she is sleeping, I usually _____ a blanket over her.

4. We _____ on the grass by the observatory and watched the meteor shower.

5. Before the meteor shower began, we _____ a tarp on the ground so that we wouldn't get wet.

6. Mr. Dodgson has often _____ awake at night, thinking about his lesson plan for the next day.

7. The Department of Public Transportation has _____ a new road around the north end of the lake.

8. Please _____ the computer cables along the wall in the computer lab so that no one will trip over them.

9. Take your shoes off, and _____ down until you feel better.

10. Before we start our research, we will _____ the old newspapers across the floor in chronological order.

LANGUAGE HANDBOOK **3** USING VERBS

WORKSHEET 9 Using *Rise* and *Raise*

EXERCISE A For each of the following sentences, underline the correct form of *rise* or *raise* in parentheses.

EXAMPLES 1. The number of students attending the games has (<u>risen</u>, raised).

2. We (<u>raised</u>, rose) our legs so that Ed could sweep under our feet.

1. Muhammad Ali (*rose*, *raised*) to fame by becoming the world heavyweight boxing champion three times.

2. The release of water from the dam will (*raise*, *rise*) the lake level by several feet.

3. The sun (*raised*, *rose*), streaking the sky with pale oranges and pinks.

4. Should we (*rise*, *raise*) our membership dues so that we can buy new equipment?

5. Howard has (*raised*, *risen*) the question of whether we need to buy a lantern.

6. The butterflies (*rose*, *raised*) from the flowering bush before settling down again.

7. Mrs. Johnson explained that yeast causes bread to (*rise*, *raise*).

8. Do you know how our team will (*raise*, *rise*) money for the storm victims?

9. Kilimanjaro (*rises*, *raises*) majestically from the plains of Tanzania, Africa.

10. Let's (*rise*, *raise*) the curtain so that we can see better.

EXERCISE B Write the correct form of *rise* or *raise* on the lines in each of the following sentences.

EXAMPLE 1. The helicopter _____*rose*_____ like a noisy whirlwind.

1. We watched the colored shapes slowly _____ and falling in the lava lamp.

2. Ancient civilizations such as Babylonia _____ to power in the valley between the Tigris and the Euphrates Rivers.

3. Did the carpenters finish _____ the floor joists before noon?

4. Carmen had to _____ her voice to be heard above the noisy crowd.

5. The popularity of ethnic foods has _____ steadily over the years.

6. The road worker _____ the orange flag as a signal to proceed with caution.

7. Grandmother _____ before dawn most days.

8. The company _____ our salaries but also increased our responsibilities.

9. The baseball fans _____ to their feet as the batter hit yet another home run.

10. In the summer, the upper stories of a house are often warmer than the first floor because hot air _____.

Elements of Literature

LANGUAGE HANDBOOK **3** **USING VERBS**

WORKSHEET 10 Test (Rules 3 a–f)

EXERCISE A   On the line provided, write the correct principal part of the italicized verb in parentheses, depending on the meaning of each sentence.

EXAMPLE ___*followed*___ **1.** When you have (*follow*) the trail to the end, turn left and you will see the lake.

_____ **1.** My aunt should have (*return*) from her business trip to Seattle this evening.

_____ **2.** The crowd is (*shout*) for the team to make a touchdown.

_____ **3.** We will (*use*) a special computer program to track the progress of the space shuttle.

_____ **4.** Please (*wipe*) your feet on the doormat before you come in.

_____ **5.** The class (*like*) reading the play *A Raisin in the Sun* at the same time that they are reading about the civil rights struggle.

_____ **6.** Ms. Cartwright had (*work*) at several schools before she came to ours.

_____ **7.** They are (*complete*) the project this afternoon.

_____ **8.** She (*smile*) when she heard the good news.

_____ **9.** Mr. Liebowitz has (*ask*) for some extra exam booklets.

_____ **10.** Our whole class is (*support*) the women's soccer team this year.

EXERCISE B   On the line provided, write the correct past or past participle form of each italicized verb in parentheses.

EXAMPLE ___*took*___ **1.** After she had missed her first flight, Ms. Sorenson (*take*) a later one.

_____ **1.** Adrienne (*see*) Martina in the apartment window yesterday.

_____ **2.** Nelson has (*chose*) to apply to more than one college.

_____ **3.** The guide (*lead*) the hikers across the stream and up the mountain before you arrived.

_____ **4.** The painters ought to have (*spread*) the paint more evenly across the side of the house.

_____ **5.** Last week Ms. Scofeld (*get*) a package in the mail from her aunt in Paraguay.

_____ **6.** (*Do*) all of you remember to set your clocks back this past weekend?

Continued ☞

_____ 7. Working together, the metal shop class (*make*) a scale model of the Eiffel Tower out of scrap metal last semester.

_____ 8. Had the marching band (*eat*) before they got on the bus last Friday?

_____ 9. Unfortunately, the movie had (*begin*) before we were able to take our seats.

_____ 10. My grandfather (*bring*) souvenirs from the Grand Canyon for all of his grandchildren.

EXERCISE C On the lines provided, rewrite each of the following sentences by changing the italicized verb or verbs to the tense indicated in parentheses.

EXAMPLE 1. Katrina *brought* potato bread for the potluck dinner. (*present perfect*) <u>Katrina has brought potato bread for the potluck dinner.</u>

1. The floodwaters *broke* through the levee, flooding much of the business district. (*past perfect*) _____

2. This season Kathleen Battle *sings* the role of Mimi in the opera La Bohème. (*present perfect*) _____

3. The lawyer *had finished* her final argument by four o'clock. (*future perfect*) _____

4. The author *works* on her short story all afternoon. (*present perfect*) _____

5. Antonio *emptied* the litter box while Paula *fed* the cat its dinner. (*present*) _____

6. Our cousin Kendall *designed* Hawaiian shirts and *marketed* them over the Internet. (*future*) _____

7. The United States Senate *will pass* a bill providing funds for highway repair. (*past*) ___

Continued ☞

8. My whole family *goes* to New Mexico for my grandfather's birthday. (*past*)

_____

_____

9. Mrs. Washington *played* organ and piano at our church for years. (*present perfect*) ___

_____

_____

10. Malcolm's family *will fly* to Mexico in the summer to see the ruins at Chichén Itzá.
(*past*) _____

_____

EXERCISE D   In the following paragraph, the verb tenses are not consistent. Decide whether the paragraph should be in the present or past tense. Then, on the lines provided, rewrite the paragraph, making sure to use consistent verb tense.

EXAMPLE [1] When Ernest Lawrence Thayer sends his poem to a newspaper, he signed his nickname "Phin."

[1] When Ernest Lawrence Thayer sent his poem to a newspaper, he signed his nickname "Phin." **or** When Ernest Lawrence Thayer sends his poem to a newspaper, he signs his nickname "Phin."

[1] "Casey at the Bat," composed by Ernest Lawrence Thayer in 1888, becomes the most famous baseball poem ever written. [2] The poem is recited around the country, and audiences loved it. [3] However, Thayer considered the poem badly written and for years does not admit he was the author. [4] Many people tried to take credit for the poem, and several baseball players say the poem was about them. [5] When the author was finally identified, he refuses to take money for the poem's many reprintings.

_____

_____

_____

_____

_____

_____

Continued ☞

LANGUAGE HANDBOOK 3 WORSHEET 10 (continued)

EXERCISE E ·On the line provided, identify the verb in each of the following sentences as *AV* for active voice or *PV* for passive voice.

EXAMPLE ___*AV*___ **1.** Both Maya Angelou and Francisco Jiménez have written short stories.

_____ **1.** Maya Angelou has written autobiographies, poems, and plays.

_____ **2.** The autobiography *I Know Why the Caged Bird Sings* was written by her.

_____ **3.** Francisco Jiménez was inspired to write by his sophomore English teacher, Miss Bell.

_____ **4.** He has won several awards for his short stories.

_____ **5.** A Ph.D. in Latin American literature was earned by Jiménez after many years of hard work.

EXERCISE F For each of the following sentences, underline the correct verb in parentheses.

EXAMPLES **1.** (*Set*, *Sit*) the plant over in that corner, please.

2. Lauren (*laid*, *lay*) down for a quick catnap.

3. The smoke (*rose*, *raised*) from the campfire.

1. Ashley reluctantly (*laid*, *lay*) down her book about the Aborigines of Australia.

2. The tired puppy could barely (*rise*, *raise*) its head after playing hard all day.

3. Grandpa usually (*sits*, *sets*) next to me at dinner.

4. Your camera is (*laying*, *lying*) on the front hall table.

5. Stock prices (*raised*, *rose*) sharply on Wall Street yesterday.

6. The baby is (*lying*, *laying*) on his back, busily kicking his legs.

7. If you (*sit*, *set*) the scanner over there, its power cord won't reach the electrical outlet.

8. Zack (*laid*, *lay*) the map on the hood of the car, and a gust of wind blew it to the ground.

9. Tibet (*lays*, *lies*) on a high plateau north of the Himalayas.

10. At half time, many fans had (*raised*, *risen*) from their seats to stretch their legs.

LANGUAGE HANDBOOK 4 USING PRONOUNS

WORKSHEET 1 Identifying and Using Pronouns in the Nominative Case (Rule 4 a)

EXERCISE On the line provided in each of the following sentences, write one personal pronoun that can replace the word or words in italics.

EXAMPLE ___She___ 1. *Hilda* brought her sister a new record.

_____ 1. *Tania Atwater* is a leading scientist.

_____ 2. *My next-door neighbors and I* went camping.

_____ 3. *Our old car* got better mileage than our new car.

_____ 4. Should *people in glass houses* throw stones?

_____ 5. *Ruth and I* are both in the school orchestra.

_____ 6. *Danny* took sailing lessons last summer.

_____ 7. What time did *Phil and Don* get home yesterday?

_____ 8. *Maria and LaVerne* are the best students in the whole school.

_____ 9. If *Mom* asks you, explain what happened.

_____ 10. *Lori and Karen* are taking French.

_____ 11. If you and *Wendy* try out for the diving team, I will, too.

_____ 12. Either Jermaine or *his brother* has the equipment bag.

_____ 13. *The girls* came home with three medals and a trophy.

_____ 14. When *Greg and the outfielders* win, they really celebrate.

_____ 15. Fortunately, *the other sprinters and I* avoided a collision.

_____ 16. *Coach Garza and the fans* cheered as the clock ran out.

_____ 17. Both Clarisse and *her mother* want the race to go on.

_____ 18. Last year, *the archery competition* was held first.

_____ 19. Will *weight lifting and deck tennis* be the newest events at the meet?

_____ 20. *Mr. Chaplinski's father* was a well-known wrestler.

_____ 21. Did *the leaves and the twigs* block the gutters?

_____ 22. What a fright *Mrs. Reynolds* gave us!

_____ 23. Here are *your keys and sunglasses.*

_____ 24. Joel and *his cousin Al* lit the menorah.

_____ 25. Gracie and Victor, where are *Gracie and Victor* hiding?

LANGUAGE HANDBOOK **4** **USING PRONOUNS**

| WORKSHEET 2 | **Identifying and Using Pronouns as Predicate Nominatives (Rule 4 b)** |

EXERCISE A   In each of the following sentences, underline the correct italicized pronoun form in parentheses.

> **EXAMPLE 1.** The player who made the final goal of the game was (*her*, <u>*she*</u>).

1. The best spellers in the class are you and (*she, her*).

2. The ones who brought the dog home must have been (*they, them*).

3. The new editor of the yearbook will be (*he, him*).

4. The people you are looking for could be (*they, them*).

5. The players in the first match will be Venus Williams and (*she, her*).

6. That must be (*she, her*) and the Jacksons in the front row.

7. If it had been Omar and (*I, me*), we would have told you.

8. The two you are talking about might possibly have been Andrea and (*he, him*), but they certainly could not have been (*we, us*).

9. If it was not (*he, him*) at the top of the stairs, I can't guess who it was.

10. The last ones to speak at the assembly were (*we, us*).

EXERCISE B   In each of the following sentences, draw a line through any incorrect pronouns and write the correct form on the line provided. If the sentence is already correct, write *C*.

> **EXAMPLE** ___*he*___ **1.** The captain of the ship is ~~him~~.

_____ **1.** The unknown caller may be he.

_____ **2.** In the book, the murderer was her.

_____ **3.** It was Anne and us who used the Sanchezes' car.

_____ **4.** No, it was they who had that noisy party.

_____ **5.** The person in charge of mowing the lawn is me.

_____ **6.** The last one we thought of was him.

_____ **7.** If it is Murray and they, ask them to come in.

_____ **8.** The next time monitors are chosen, they might be us.

_____ **9.** Our only winner was him.

_____ **10.** If you were me, what would you do?

LANGUAGE HANDBOOK **4** **USING PRONOUNS**

WORKSHEET 3 | **Using Pronouns as Direct Objects (Rule 4 c)**

EXERCISE In each of the following sentences, underline the correct italicized pronoun form in parentheses.

> **EXAMPLE 1.** We saw Chris and (*he*, <u>*him*</u>) at the bookstore yesterday.

1. Mrs. Rosen took Becky, two other girls, and (*I, me*) to the movies.

2. He and I saw you and (*they, them*) before anyone else.

3. Tanisha instructed (*them, they*) in the use of the microwave oven.

4. Do your parents want you and (*we, us*) home early tonight?

5. Please don't leave (*he, him*) and his dog out in the rain.

6. You should have made Jill or (*she, her*) the announcer.

7. We should bring the girls and (*he, him*) back to the school in our car.

8. The manager will interview (*he, him*) or (*she, her*) first.

9. The Drakes will meet you and (*I, me*) at the main gate.

10. I surprised Jacqueline and (*her, she*) with a Dr. Seuss book.

11. Randall saw my brother and (*he, him*) in the mystery section at the library.

12. Aunt Lorena told (*we, us*) about her childhood in Utah.

13. The conductor placed (*them, they*) and (*me, I*) between the piano and the string section.

14. If swimming after a meal worries you or (*she, her*), you shouldn't do so.

15. Nia asked Daniel and (*she, her*) if they wanted to come to the meeting.

16. Mrs. Wyatt introduced (*we, us*) to the pleasures of classical music.

17. The taxi driver dropped Dr. Borges and (*him, he*) in front of our house.

18. The basic carpentry class saved (*her, she*) and (*I, me*) from several time-consuming and costly mistakes.

19. The idea of travel to distant planets intrigued (*they, them*) and (*me, I*).

20. Ms. Kaimowitz asked Francesca and (*her, she*) for their homework assignments.

21. The instructions for the model airplane confused Gustav and (*I, me*).

22. Howard's parents picked up Howard and (*us, we*) on Sunday night.

23. Would you help Bruce and (*me, I*) while we put the canoe in the water?

24. Claire found Susan and (*they, them*) in front of the theater.

25. The conclusion of the television miniseries thrilled my parents and (*we, us*).

NAME _____ CLASS _____ DATE _____

| WORSHEET 4 | Using Pronouns in the Objective Case (Rules 4 c–e)

EXERCISE   For each of the following sentences, write the correct pronoun form in parentheses on the line provided.

EXAMPLE _them_ **1.** You know the first computers were big, if you've seen photos of (*they, them*).

_____ **1.** The size of old computers may seem funny to (*us, we*) today.

_____ **2.** It took a great deal of energy to power (*they, them*).

_____ **3.** Imagine the early engineers being happy with machines that gave (*they, them*) only twenty or thirty calculations a second!

_____ **4.** Since the 1950s, designers have created smaller computers for (*we, us*).

_____ **5.** Today's professional may carry a laptop with (*he or she, him or her*).

_____ **6.** Most of (*we, us*) find laptops easy to use.

_____ **7.** Computers help (*we, us*) by making 250 million calculations per second!

_____ **8.** Without computers, most of (*us, we*) would still be relying on long division.

_____ **9.** A teacher may ask you to work such problems for (*he or she, him or her*).

_____ **10.** What further computer developments are left for (*we, us*)?

_____ **11.** Many high school graduates go into fields of study that will lead (*they, them*) toward answers to such an intriguing question.

_____ **12.** Students were pleased when a technology expert visited (*they, them*).

_____ **13.** Even those of (*us, we*) in middle school enjoy special career activities.

_____ **14.** Both of the Murchison twins took lists of questions with (*they, them*).

_____ **15.** Randy and Sandy sat next to my friend and (*I, me*) in the auditorium.

_____ **16.** Young and enthusiastic, the speaker inspired the other students and (*I, me*).

_____ **17.** Sandy has decided that the technical institute is the school for (*her, she*).

_____ **18.** The speaker from the institute gave Randy and (*she, her*) several brochures.

_____ **19.** They gave their names so that the institute could contact (*they, them*).

_____ **20.** It's easy for my friends and (*I, me*) to find the institute's Web site, too.

_____ **21.** Computer companies want skilled technicians working for (*they, them*).

_____ **22.** Technology gives (*we, us*) career choices never dreamed of decades ago.

_____ **23.** Imagine the size of radios Grandma saw around (*she, her*) as a child.

_____ **24.** Transistors and integrated circuits changed life for her and (*we, us*).

_____ **25.** Can you see (*me, I*) as the next big innovator in technology?

Elements of Literature

LANGUAGE HANDBOOK **4** **USING PRONOUNS**

| WORKSHEET 5 | ## Using Pronouns as Objects of Prepositions (Rule 4 e) |

EXERCISE   In each of the following sentences, underline the correct italicized pronoun form in parentheses.

> **EXAMPLE 1.** I gave the books to Brian and (<u>*her*</u>, *she*) after class.

1. Can you come to the game with David and (*me, I*)?

2. I spoke to Lisa and (*her, she*) at our party.

3. Edith will go downtown with both Jean and (*she, her*).

4. These old books are for my cousin and (*I, me*).

5. Dan's mother received postcards from (*him, he*) and Bernardo.

6. Gordon is traveling in Mexico with Pete and (*they, them*).

7. Natalie brought these magazines for Diane and (*us, we*).

8. The letter was addressed to (*him, he*) and (*her, she*).

9. All of (*them, they*) are in the play with Don and (*I, me*).

10. I spoke to Inez and (*he, him*) about practicing after school.

11. The magazine was of interest to Sylvia and (*I, me*).

12. Because of Stacey and (*him, he*) the fire was reported in time.

13. Bess, will you wait for Jocelyn and (*we, us*) after school?

14. The committee will have a conference with Ms. Epstein and (*I, me*).

15. Yesterday I sat between (*her, she*) and Elaine at the game.

16. You will have to choose between (*he, him*) and (*I, me*).

17. I sat across from you and (*him, he*).

18. Please line up behind (*her, she*) and (*him, he*).

19. I asked Sarah and her about Fritz and (*they, them*).

20. We thought everybody knew about the Baxters and (*we, us*).

21. The box that we received from John and (*he, him*) was well wrapped.

22. Between (*we, us*), there are no secrets.

23. I plan to vote for (*she, her*) for class president.

24. We were able to attend the concert because of the efforts of (*he, him*) and his father.

25. According to (*she, her*) and Marvel, the sweet corn should be cooked soon after it is picked.

LANGUAGE
HANDBOOK **4** USING PRONOUNS

WORKSHEET 6 | Using *Who* and *Whom* and Reflexive Pronouns

EXERCISE A   In each of the following sentences, underline the correct italicized pronoun form in parentheses.

EXAMPLE **1.** We didn't know (<u>*who*</u>, *whom*) was invited to the induction.

1. Olivia, (*who, whom*) I nominated for treasurer, won the election easily.

2. (*Who, Whom*) will Serge introduce to the audience?

3. You may recognize the name of the celebrity (*who, whom*) will speak briefly.

4. Mr. Chang and Ms. Reynolds are the teachers (*who, whom*) you should consult.

5. Any students (*who, whom*) are interested in the council's activities should attend the first meeting.

6. Please welcome our new officers, many of (*who, whom*) were representatives just last year.

7. Our faculty sponsors, (*who, whom*) have helped us organize, deserve a hand.

8. I hope that the people (*who, whom*) promised to bring snacks won't forget.

9. (*Who, Whom*) besides Kenyata will be serving punch at the reception?

10. It is easy to see (*who, whom*) has earned the respect and trust of the other students.

EXERCISE B   For each of the following sentences, write the correct pronoun form in parentheses on the line provided.

EXAMPLE _*himself*_ **1.** Leon asked (*hisself, himself*) why he had lost his temper.

_____ **1.** The nervous actors had not prepared (*theirselves, themselves*) well.

_____ **2.** I often remind (*me, myself*) to think before I speak.

_____ **3.** Dr. Torres and (*myself, I*) believe your essay will get published.

_____ **4.** The toddler helped (*hisself, himself*) to the fortune cookies.

_____ **5.** Rescue workers positioned (*theirselves, themselves*) above the tent.

_____ **6.** Abdul and (*I, myself*) volunteered to laminate posters.

_____ **7.** I can only speak for (*me, myself*) when I admit carelessness.

_____ **8.** You and Senator Hertzog will seat (*yourselves, yourself*) by the podium.

_____ **9.** When it comes to grooming horses, you can count on (*myself, me*).

_____ **10.** Mr. Dodd reminded (*hisself, himself*) to pick up his dry cleaning.

| WORKSHEET 7 | **More Practice with Pronouns** |

EXERCISE A   In each of the following sentences, underline the correct form of the italicized pronouns in parentheses.

 EXAMPLE **1.** It is important that (*us*, <u>*we*</u>) students appreciate geography.

1. How many of (*us*, *we*) eighth-graders can locate New Zealand on a map?

2. (*Us*, *We*) experts even know about New Zealand's first inhabitants, the Maori.

3. Some of (*we*, *us*) geography enthusiasts know a good deal about Maori culture.

4. The woodcarvings of the Maori impress many of (*us*, *we*) art students.

5. Is New Zealand's capital, Wellington, familiar to (*us*, *we*) scholars?

6. Please give (*us*, *we*) pupils of geography time to learn the details.

7. (*We*, *Us*) map readers cope frequently with changing borders and names.

8. Wellington sounds like a British name to many of (*us*, *we*) students.

9. It would not surprise (*we*, *us*) historians to learn that New Zealand was ruled for a time by the British.

10. (*We*, *Us*) teenagers already know that history and geography go hand in hand.

EXERCISE B   For each of the following sentences, write the correct pronoun form in parentheses on the line provided.

 EXAMPLE ___*we*___ **1.** Do you want to know whether (*us*, *we*) choir members enjoyed the trip?

_____ **1.** Why things went wrong depends on (*who*, *whom*) you ask.

_____ **2.** The parents (*who*, *whom*) chaperoned said it was just the season for colds.

_____ **3.** Originally, (*we*, *us*) singers looked forward to the bus trip to Colorado.

_____ **4.** The first snifflers hate to put the blame on (*theirselves*, *themselves*).

_____ **5.** By the time (*us*, *we*) contestants reached Amarillo, everyone on the bus was coughing.

_____ **6.** Everyone remembered to bring a coat except for (*me*, *myself*).

_____ **7.** The girl (*who*, *whom*) I sat next to said she caught my cold.

_____ **8.** She and (*myself*, *I*) both sing soprano.

_____ **9.** The professionals (*whom*, *who*) judged us tried to be polite.

_____ **10.** One asked if the soloists could hear (*theirselves*, *themselves*) for all the sneezing.

LANGUAGE HANDBOOK 4 USING PRONOUNS

WORKSHEET 8 | Test (Rules 4 a–e)

EXERCISE A On each of the numbered lines in the following paragraph, write the correct pronoun in parentheses.

> EXAMPLE Most of [1] __us__ (*we, us*) students already know
> Louisiana has a French heritage.

My grandfather, [1] _____ (*who, whom*) is from St. Martinville, Louisiana, loves to talk about his Cajun background. Granny and [2] _____ (*he, him*) both have French Canadian ancestry. Granddad and [3] _____ (*her, she*) have been married for almost fifty years. They send my brothers and [4] _____ (*me, I*) photos and articles showing the French influence in their state. [5] _____ (*Us, We*) members of the younger generation didn't know that the word *Cajun* comes from *Acadian,* a member of the French colony in eastern Canada settled four hundred years ago. Apparently, French-speaking colonists, [6] _____ (*who, whom*) were proud of their language and customs, did not want to embrace the dominant English culture. In 1713, forced into exile by their new rulers, [7] _____ (*they, them*) embarked on a long exodus to Louisiana and other places more hospitable to the French. Granny says that [8] _____ (*she, her*) and other people from the St. Martinville area always used to read in school about Evangeline, the heroine of Longfellow's epic poem. If it had been up to [9] _____ (*me, myself*), I doubt I could have maintained perfect loyalty over the heartbreaking trip from Canada to Louisiana. Today, you can see for [10] _____ (*you, yourself*) a statue of Evangeline Bellefontaine in the town of St. Martinville.

EXERCISE B On the line provided, identify the italicized pronoun in each of the following sentences as *SUBJ* for subject, *PRED NOM* for predicate nominative, *DO* for direct object, or *OP* for object of a preposition.

> EXAMPLE __SUBJ__ 1. *We* read aloud from one of Robert Frost's books.

_____ 1. Many of *us* consider Robert Frost one of America's finest modern poets.

_____ 2. It is *he* whom most people think of first when American poetry is mentioned.

_____ 3. *He* has been popular for three generations.

_____ 4. Most people like *him* for the surface clarity of his poems.

Continued ☞

_____ 5. With a second or third reading, however, *we* discover depths of meaning.

_____ 6. Actually, *he* is as profound as other poets who seem more difficult.

_____ 7. On Inauguration Day in 1960, Frost received the official recognition that *he* had long deserved.

_____ 8. Bareheaded in the chilling wind, he recited his poem "The Gift Outright" to all of *us* across the nation.

_____ 9. In the same dry, weary voice, *he* read his poems to thousands of young people and adults.

_____ 10. People all over the world will remember *him* for his poems and his way of talking about life.

EXERCISE C Underline each correct italicized pronoun form in parentheses.

      EXAMPLE 1. My aunt gave Dave, Inez, and (*I, me*) tickets to the amusement park.

1. Dave, Inez, and (*me, I*) went to the amusement park on Memorial Day.

2. Inez asked Dave and (*I, me*) whether we would go on the roller coaster.

3. Inez and (*he, him*) had never ridden a roller coaster before.

4. When we went down the first dip, Dave grabbed (*her, she*) and yelled.

5. I suggested the bumper cars to (*they, them*).

6. Dave and I rode in a separate car from Inez and kept bumping into (*she, her*).

7. Inez asked (*us, we*) if we would buy tickets for the Ferris wheel.

8. Dave and I talked (*she, her*) into trying the haunted house.

9. When a ghost jumped out, (*we, us*) all screamed.

10. Fireworks were set off at dusk, and (*them, they*) were the best part of the day.

EXERCISE D Draw a line through any incorrect personal pronoun form in the following sentences, and write the correct form on the line provided. If the sentence is already correct, write *C*.

      EXAMPLE ___He___ **1.** ~~Him~~ and I saw the meteor.

_____ 1. Are these pencils for them or I?

_____ 2. Us and the ninth-graders have been especially busy this week.

_____ 3. It was they who complimented Priscilla and me on our work.

_____ 4. Bernice is staying for a conference with Mr. Crowley and I.

_____ 5. The Murphy twins have invited Carole and he to a picnic.

Continued ☞

Elements of Literature

EXERCISE E   For each of the following sentences, underline the correct italicized pronoun form in parentheses.

> **EXAMPLE 1.** Raymond often surprises (*hisself,* <u>*himself*</u>) with his memory of old films.

1. Toni and Gary both pride (*theirselves, themselves*) on their writing.

2. Charlie, the narrator of the story, notices (*hisself, himself*) getting smarter.

3. (*Us, We*) avid readers always expect an ironic twist from the stories of Roald Dahl.

4. (*Who, Whom*) imprisoned Yoshiko Uchida's family during World War II, the Japanese government or the United States government?

5. Of all the authors read by (*us, we*) horror story fans, Edgar Allan Poe is the best.

6. Did you ask (*you, yourself*) where the people went in Ray Bradbury's story "There Will Come Soft Rains"?

7. Someone in class felt sorry for the man on (*who, whom*) the character plays her joke.

8. Shel Silverstein has a way of making (*me, myself*) laugh.

9. Anne Frank did not take many belongings with (*her, herself*) into hiding.

10. The author O. Henry, (*who, whom*) is my favorite writer, wrote the story "The Ransom of Red Chief."

EXERCISE F   In each of the following sentences, draw a line through any incorrect pronouns and write the correct pronoun form on the line provided. If the sentence is already correct, write *C*.

> **EXAMPLE** ___*her*___ **1.** I had never been introduced to Jacob and ~~she~~ before.

_____ **1.** The argument between Geraldo and I was not serious.

_____ **2.** The stories written by Jaime and her were the best.

_____ **3.** The newspaper story was about his tennis partner and he.

_____ **4.** To my parents and us the movie was disappointing.

_____ **5.** We received letters from the Rileys and they.

_____ **6.** Someone has been looking for Greta and we.

_____ **7.** Who was sitting beside you and he?

_____ **8.** Are you going to the game with Arno and I?

_____ **9.** Everyone was on time except you and them.

_____ **10.** I have confidence in Sarah and her.

LANGUAGE HANDBOOK 5 USING MODIFIERS

WORKSHEET 1 | **Identifying and Using Modifiers in Regular and Irregular Comparisons (Rules 5 a, b)**

EXERCISE A   In each of the following sentences, underline the correct italicized comparison in parentheses.

> **EXAMPLE 1.** Which shines (*brightlier*, <u>*more brightly*</u>), a nova or a supernova?

1. A light-year is (*more far, farther*) than a trillion miles.

2. To me, black holes are (*more intriguing, most intriguing*) than doughnut holes.

3. What is the (*more distant, most distant*) star you can name?

4. Fortunately, our planet is not any (*more close, closer*) to the sun.

5. The idea of a flat world sounds (*more strange, stranger*) today than it did centuries ago.

6. The (*most good, best*) grade my mother ever made was on one astronomy test.

7. She had to study (*harder, more hard*) than ever to end up with an A.

8. Now she is one of the (*respectedest, most respected*) astronomers.

9. No one describes a dwarf star (*more well, better*) than Mom does.

10. Of all the sciences, astronomy challenges my imagination the (*more, most*).

EXERCISE B   For each of the following sentences, identify the degree of comparison (positive, comparative, or superlative) of the word or words in italics on the line provided.

> **EXAMPLES** <u>*comparative*</u> **1.** Gina is *more generous* than I am.
>
>   <u>*positive*</u> **2.** Langford Creek still runs *clearly* in the hills.

_____ **1.** The newspaper said it was the *worst* hailstorm ever.

_____ **2.** Juan has *more important* things to do than watch TV.

_____ **3.** How *well* can you sing the national anthem?

_____ **4.** Twenty years ago, meteorologists predicted the weather *less accurately* than they do now.

_____ **5.** Clarence logs on to the Internet *more often* than Dwayne.

_____ **6.** We take Scruffy to the *gentlest* veterinarian.

_____ **7.** Sometimes I'm the world's *worst* first-base player.

_____ **8.** Velvet feels *more luxurious* than terry cloth.

_____ **9.** The teacher tiptoed *silently* among the sleeping kindergartners.

_____ **10.** Isn't this Cupcake's *cutest* litter of kittens?

LANGUAGE HANDBOOK **5** USING MODIFIERS

WORKSHEET 2 Using Modifiers Correctly (Rules 5 a, b)

EXERCISE A In each of the following sentences, underline the correct italicized modifier in parentheses.

> **EXAMPLE 1.** Of the two choices on the menu, I would say that the curry is (*better*, *best*).

1. Of all the farmer's problems, drought is the (*worse*, *worst*).

2. The homesteader thought it was (*best*, *better*) to settle in the river valley than on the hill.

3. Of all the Colonial heroes, Paul Revere is one of the (*more famous*, *most famous*).

4. The hawk swooped down (*more*, *most*) furiously than before.

5. Who is (*more curious*, *most curious*), you or Alice?

6. The snow fell (*less*, *least*) quickly after the cold front passed.

7. Compassion is one of the (*more important*, *most important*) values in many faiths.

8. The monsoons bring the (*heaviest*, *heavier*) rains of the year in India.

9. Conrad's fever was (*worst*, *worse*) in the evening than in the morning.

10. If you perform (*better*, *best*) than you have, you may advance to the finals.

EXERCISE B For each of the following sentences, write the correct italicized modifier in parentheses on the line provided.

> **EXAMPLE** ____More____ **1.** (*More*, *Most*) geologists than ever are studying the earth's surface.

_____ 1. The (*largest*, *larger*) crater on the moon is about 700 miles wide.

_____ 2. Even (*deepest*, *deeper*) craters may have scarred the earth long ago.

_____ 3. Iron meteorites are (*stronger*, *strongest*) than rock meteorites.

_____ 4. Earth's surface is (*more new*, *newer*) than the rest of the planet.

_____ 5. The continents would fit together (*most snugly*, *more snugly*) than you might think.

_____ 6. What is the (*most gigantic*, *more gigantic*) sheet of ice you can imagine?

_____ 7. Of all a geologist's task, I think the search for new energy sources is the (*more interesting*, *most interesting*).

_____ 8. Is it (*good*, *better*) that petroleum geologists continue searching for oil?

_____ 9. Which of the two theories of continental drift is (*better*, *best*)?

_____ 10. The (*highest*, *higher*) mountain peaks can look like islands when seen from a distance.

LANGUAGE HANDBOOK **5** **USING MODIFIERS**

WORKSHEET 3 Using *Other* and *Else;* Avoiding Double Comparisons and Double Negatives (Rules 5 c, d)

EXERCISE A In each of the following sentences, underline the nonstandard comparison and write the standard form on the line provided.

EXAMPLE *any other boy* **1.** Carlos is smarter than any boy in class.

_____ **1.** I think "The Monkey's Paw" is scarier than any story in the book.

_____ **2.** You paint better than anyone in the studio.

_____ **3.** Poetry is more rhythmic than any kind of literature.

_____ **4.** That civil rights marcher was braver than anyone.

_____ **5.** The Civil War era was probably more difficult than any time in our country's history.

_____ **6.** She can write more clearly than anyone.

_____ **7.** Mark Twain was more outspoken than any writer of his time.

_____ **8.** Gary enjoys reading more than anything.

_____ **9.** Mr. Van Daan was more selfish than any character in the play.

_____ **10.** I think O. Henry is more humorous than any writer.

EXERCISE B For each of the following sentences, underline the double comparison or double negative and write the standard form on the line provided.

EXAMPLE _can't ever_ **1.** You can't never tell what a baby is thinking.

_____ **1.** However, there can't be no doubt that little Howie is smart.

_____ **2.** He is more readier to talk than I was at age two.

_____ **3.** You won't never guess what he can already do.

_____ **4.** I can't hardly wait to tell you.

_____ **5.** The answer is more odder than you might think.

_____ **6.** One day I couldn't find my homework nowhere.

_____ **7.** Howie was more quieter than usual.

_____ **8.** I couldn't scarcely believe he had my math paper.

_____ **9.** He had made the most funniest mark with a crayon.

_____ **10.** Nobody had never given me a one hundred in math before.

LANGUAGE HANDBOOK 5 USING MODIFIERS

WORKSHEET 4 | **Correcting Misplaced Modifiers (Rule 5 e)**

EXERCISE   On the lines provided, rewrite each of the following sentences so that the misplaced modifier is corrected. If the sentence is already correct, write *C*.

EXAMPLE **1.** Donnie had just sat down by the tree with his lunch. *With his lunch, Donnie had just sat down by the tree.*

1. He would pitch his final ballgame tonight, hoping for a chance to play for the all-stars.

_____

_____

2. He had promised himself he would not be nervous at the game that morning. _____

_____

_____

3. Donnie's sandwich tasted good that he had made the night before. _____

_____

_____

4. He looked up at the birds trying not to think about the game in the tree. _____

_____

_____

5. Looking back at him, he noticed a male cardinal. _____

_____

6. The brilliant red bird seemed to tilt his head toward Donnie on the limb. _____

_____

_____

7. Donnie looked for a nest leaning against the trunk. _____

_____

8. He was puzzled by the presence of the cardinal finding no signs of other birds. _____

_____

_____

9. Then he could see the bird's beak open from the corner of his eye. _____

_____

_____

Continued ☞

10. The most pleasant melody floated down to the boy from the cardinal. _____
_____

11. Suddenly, two of Donnie's teammates ran toward him, scaring off the bird. _____
_____
_____

12. They asked him if he was going to pitch a no-hitter as they approached. _____
_____
_____

13. He joked that he was going to walk all the batters finishing his sandwich. _____
_____
_____

14. Donnie suggested they head for the cafeteria without mentioning the bird. _____
_____
_____

15. Even through his afternoon classes, however, the bird came to mind in the tree. _____
_____
_____

16. That night Donnie dressed in the locker room among his teammates growing less
worried about the outcome of the game. _____
_____

17. Thinking of a single purpose, he would go out on the pitcher's mound. _____
_____
_____

18. If he could tell himself he had played well, he would be happy in the morning. _____
_____
_____

19. There was no way of predicting how a final decision would turn out on the all-stars.
_____
_____

20. Still, Donnie felt lucky walking out on the field wearing a bright red cap. _____
_____

Elements of Literature

WORSHEET 5	**Correcting Dangling and Misplaced Modifiers (Rule 5 e)**

EXERCISE On the lines provided, rewrite each of the following sentences so that the dangling or misplaced modifier is corrected.

> EXAMPLE 1. Asked to recommend a funny story, one of O. Henry's came to mind. *Asked to recommend a funny story, I thought of one by O. Henry.*

1. Wanting to get rich quickly, a plan to kidnap a boy occurred to some men. _____

2. Kicking and fighting, trouble was all the boy caused. _____

3. Whining hungrily, dinner was quickly served to the child. _____

4. Having finally dozed off, screams awoke one kidnapper at daybreak. _____

5. Terrified and humiliated, the boy's attack had surprised the other man. _____

6. Fearing the parents wouldn't pay, the plan looked less wise to the kidnappers. _____

7. Pestering and threatening everyone, who wouldn't want a vacation from the boy? _____

8. Going on his way to collect the ransom, it isn't clear what the kidnapper will find. _____

9. Using exaggeration and irony, you expect O. Henry's story to get funnier. _____

10. Not wanting to spoil the surprise, the conclusion should be kept secret. _____

Continued ☞

11. Being familiar with O. Henry, an ending with a twist is to be expected. _____

_____

_____

12. Using irony to create humor, O. Henry's stories are filled with contrast. _____

_____

_____

13. Filled with colorful characters, O. Henry describes his and others' experiences in his
stories. _____

_____

_____

14. Describing victims of fate, his characters have tragic and lonely lives. _____

_____

_____

15. Writing many stories in prison, the underworld life was a source of material. _____

_____

_____

16. In spite of a short and tragic life, O. Henry's stories were often humorous. _____

_____

_____

17. Marked by a little sadness mixed with humor, you may appreciate O. Henry's style. __

_____

_____

18. Interested in humorous writers, their biographies fascinate me. _____

_____

_____

19. Wanting to find a collection of his work, the library is a good place to start. _____

_____

_____

20. After checking the table of contents, several titles may look familiar. _____

_____

_____

LANGUAGE HANDBOOK	**5**	USING MODIFIERS

WORKSHEET 6 | Test (Rules 5 a–e)

EXERCISE A For each of the following sentences, underline the correct italicized modifier in parentheses.

> **EXAMPLE 1.** Harriet Tubman may be better known than (*any*, *any other*) abolitionist.

1. Perhaps the (*most familiar*, *more familiar*) dinosaur is the tyrannosaurus.

2. Carbohydrates provide more energy than (*any*, *any other*) food.

3. The United States Constitution made civil rights (*more secure*, *more securer*).

4. Some folks (*can hardly*, *can't hardly*) wait to kiss the Blarney stone.

5. Is the Yangtze the (*most long*, *longest*) river in China?

6. Sitting Bull may have been braver than (*anyone*, *anyone else*).

7. A solar eclipse (*will never*, *won't never*) happen two days in a row.

8. Cotton is (*less dense*, *less denser*) than lead.

9. You won't find (*any*, *no*) fault with Einstein's arithmetic.

10. The acoustics in our new auditorium are (*better*, *best*) for speaking than for singing.

EXERCISE B For each of the following sentences, underline the misplaced or dangling modifier. If a sentence is already correct, write *C* on the line provided.

> **EXAMPLES** _____ **1.** <u>Running toward the goal post</u>, victory seemed certain.
>
> ____*C*____ **2.** Interested in oceanography, La Shay returned to the coast.

_____ **1.** Balancing on the high dive, the water below looked inviting.

_____ **2.** Without blaming anyone, cooperation was encouraged by both principals.

_____ **3.** Eager to please, the puppy scampered back to its owner.

_____ **4.** Dr. Samani said after next semester that he was retiring.

_____ **5.** The girl rode her bicycle down the street with red hair.

_____ **6.** David heard a fly buzzing as he daydreamed.

_____ **7.** Families were evacuated from their homes on both sides of the state line.

_____ **8.** Tired of listening to excuses, Coach Berrin told us to run laps.

_____ **9.** The wind in the trees seemed magical to the child at the window.

_____ **10.** Looking up, the clouds appeared menacing to Toni.

Continued ☞

EXERCISE C   For each of the following sentences, underline the correct italicized modifier in parentheses.

> **EXAMPLE 1.** Mahatma Gandhi used the most (*peacefulest*, *peaceful*) methods of persuasion.

1. The (*highest, higher*) the interest rate is, the greater the cost of a loan.

2. Tightrope walkers perform the (*more stupendous, most stupendous*) acts.

3. Perhaps the (*better, best*) known environmentalist of her generation is Rachel Carson.

4. Maya calendars were as accurate as (*any, any other*) calendars of that time.

5. Are the skies here (*more blue, bluer*) than in other countries?

6. The Nobel Prize in physics (*couldn't hardly, could hardly*) have gone to anyone but Guglielmo Marconi.

7. Mexico City is larger than (*any, any other*) city in Mexico.

8. Deciduous trees are (*most beautiful, more beautiful*) in autumn than they are the rest of the year.

9. Caesar hadn't (*ever, never*) doubted Brutus until it was too late.

10. Rudy was better at mapping Indonesia than (*anyone, anyone else*).

EXERCISE D   On the lines in the following paragraph, write *I* to indicate sentences with misplaced or dangling modifiers. Write *C* for any sentences that are correct.

> **EXAMPLE** [1] __*I*__ Not wanting to miss the bus, the corner was crowded with students.

[1] _____ With a growing sense that she had forgotten something, the bus came down the street toward Kendra and the others. [2] _____ Kendra realized she had forgotten her lunch at that instant. [3] _____ Nervous about whether she would make it in time, her front door seemed a long way away to Kendra. [4] _____ Digging into her pocket, another frustrating mistake dawned on her. [5] _____ In the rush to get out of the house, she had left her keys on the kitchen counter. [6] _____ On the verge of tears, the race back down the sidewalk took Kendra's breath away. [7] _____ Earlier than usual, the bus pulled away seconds before she came back. [8] _____ Kendra bravely promised herself by afternoon that she would somehow turn this bad start around. [9] _____ Then from close by she heard a familiar voice. [10] _____ Having returned home for his own briefcase, her father was wondering if she needed a ride.

LANGUAGE HANDBOOK 6 PHRASES

WORKSHEET 1 | Identifying Prepositional Phrases (Rules 6 a–d)

EXERCISE A   On the line provided, identify each of the following word groups by writing *PHR* if the word group is a prepositional phrase and *NP* if it is not a prepositional phrase.

EXAMPLE   _PHR_   **1.** over the mountain

_____ **1.** in the kitchen

_____ **2.** with my bicycle

_____ **3.** Talbot and him

_____ **4.** across the highway

_____ **5.** Mrs. Lindenmeyer is reading my book report

_____ **6.** under a harvest moon

_____ **7.** beyond the solar system

_____ **8.** when I was six

_____ **9.** over the river

_____ **10.** into the trees

EXERCISE B   Underline each prepositional phrase, and circle the preposition.

EXAMPLE **1.** The longest river (in) North America is the Mississippi.

1. I am reading a book about the Columbia River.

2. The river begins in the Canadian Rocky Mountains.

3. The entire length of this mighty river is 1,240 miles.

4. The Yakima tell a story that explains why the river narrows at The Dalles.

5. The Yakima Indian Reservation is located near the Columbia River.

6. During the Ice Age the Columbia River had a different course.

7. The Grand Coulee may be the old riverbed of the Columbia.

8. Last summer we traveled through the Grand Coulee region.

9. We went to the Grand Coulee Dam.

10. The Grand Coulee Dam is located in Washington.

LANGUAGE HANDBOOK 6 PHRASES

WORKSHEET 2 Identifying and Using Adjective Phrases (Rule 6 c)

EXERCISE A In the following paragraph, underline each adjective phrase. Then, draw an arrow to the word it modifies. There are ten adjective phrases to identify. Not every sentence contains an adjective phrase. If a sentence does not contain an adjective phrase, write *NONE* above the sentence.

EXAMPLE [1] The original home of salsa and merengue music is the Caribbean.

[1] Juan Luís Guerra is a well-known singer from the Dominican Republic. [2] During the 1980s and 1990s, he became internationally known. [3] His music is a blend of two popular Caribbean styles, salsa and merengue. [4] Guerra often writes lyrics about social issues in the Dominican Republic and Latin America. [5] His music is influenced by the roots of other Caribbean and African styles of music. [6] Guerra was born and raised in a middle-class neighborhood in Santo Domingo, the capital of the Dominican Republic. [7] He studied music at a college in Boston, Massachusetts, then returned to his country. [8] One of his albums won a Grammy Award in 1991.

EXERCISE B On each line provided, write a sentence that includes the given noun or pronoun, followed by an adjective phrase. Try not to use the same preposition twice.

EXAMPLE 1. the sandals *The sandals under the bed are too small for me.*

1. someone _____

_____

2. an author _____

_____

3. the map _____

_____

4. the stars _____

_____

5. each _____

_____

LANGUAGE HANDBOOK 6 PHRASES

WORKSHEET 3 | **Identifying and Using Adverb Phrases (Rule 6 d)**

EXERCISE A   In the following paragraph, underline each adverb phrase. Then, draw an arrow to the word or words it modifies. There are ten adverb phrases to identify. Not every sentence contains an adverb phrase. If the sentence does not contain an adverb phrase, write *NONE* above the sentence.

EXAMPLE [1] Most workers in the United States do not work <u>on Labor Day</u>.

[1] Labor Day is celebrated on the first Monday in September. [2] The purpose of the celebration is to honor the working class. [3] A labor organization called the Knights of Labor initiated Labor Day in the United States. [4] In 1882, this labor organization held a large parade in New York City. [5] Two years later the group held a parade on the first Monday in September and passed a resolution to call the day Labor Day. [6] Later, worker organizations campaigned in other states to have the day declared a legal holiday. [7] During the next few years, a law to that effect was passed in four states. [8] In 1894, the U.S. Congress declared the day a legal holiday. [9] Today, Labor Day is celebrated with parades and speeches by labor leaders and political figures.

EXERCISE B   On each line provided, write a sentence using the given italicized adverb phrase. Then, circle the word that the phrase modifies.

EXAMPLE **1.** *in a hurry* The teacher (left) the classroom in a hurry and
forgot her briefcase.

1. *without leaving home* _____

_____

2. *for more than two hours* _____

_____

3. *according to the teacher* _____

_____

4. *around ten o'clock* _____

_____

5. *during the last century* _____

_____

LANGUAGE HANDBOOK **6** **PHRASES**

WORKSHEET 4 | **Identifying Present and Past Participles and Participial Phrases (Rules 6 e, f)**

EXERCISE A Underline each present participle or participial phrase in the following sentences, and circle the word or words that the participle or participial phrase modifies. If a sentence does not contain a present participle or a participial phrase, write *NONE* on the line provided.

> EXAMPLES _____ **1.** The <u>roaring</u> (lion) frightened the young child.
>
> _NONE_ **2.** My father is running every day now.

_____ **1.** The growing popularity of the Internet is catching the attention of people who sell goods and services.

_____ **2.** Peacefully floating on the lake, Rob and Lucio forgot about the horseback ride at two o'clock.

_____ **3.** Hundreds of flood evacuees were arriving at the Red Cross camp each day.

_____ **4.** The young boy was walking much faster than his braying donkey.

_____ **5.** Ahmed, eagerly expecting a letter from his best friend, waited impatiently for the mail carrier.

_____ **6.** By the time he was six years old, Wolfgang Amadeus Mozart was composing music.

_____ **7.** Wanting to commemorate the primates at the Philadelphia Zoo, the artist Sally Linder painted fourteen portraits of them.

_____ **8.** Pieter, a foreign exchange student who is living in Texas, misses the changing colors of leaves in autumn.

_____ **9.** Our neighbors are building a deck in their back yard.

_____ **10.** Studying French literature, Jan's sister decided to become a translator.

EXERCISE B Underline each past participle or participial phrase in the following sentences, and circle the word or words that the participle or participial phrase modifies. If a sentence does not contain a past participle or a participial phrase, write *NONE* on the line provided.

> EXAMPLES _____ **1.** <u>Faded by the sun</u>, the velour (curtains) had lost much of their splendor.
>
> _NONE_ **2.** The project was evaluated by several experts.

_____ **1.** Born in New Orleans in 1961, Wynton Marsalis is a Grammy Award–winning trumpet player.

_____ **2.** Soundly defeated, the soldiers laid down their weapons.

Continued ☞

_____ **3.** In the mid-1800s, the soprano Jenny Lind was known as the "Swedish Nightingale."

_____ **4.** Elyssa walked away slowly with wounded pride.

_____ **5.** The unanswered letter lay at the bottom of the drawer.

_____ **6.** The old tractor, broken and forgotten, was still in the barn.

_____ **7.** Myanmar, located in Southeast Asia, was formerly called Burma.

_____ **8.** Federico García Lorca is considered by some to be the most popular poet of the Spanish-speaking world.

_____ **9.** The contract, written in German, was found among Mr. Bohr's belongings.

_____ **10.** Now also cultivated in the United States, the kiwi fruit is named after a flightless brown bird of New Zealand.

_____ **11.** Heidi, encouraged by the audience's applause, decided to sing another song.

_____ **12.** Ashamed of his rudeness to his mother's visitor, Rudy took a deep breath and apologized to the woman.

_____ **13.** The farmer, completely exhausted by his twelve-hour day in the field, ate a hearty supper.

_____ **14.** The surprised burglar dropped his tools and loot and ran out the back door.

_____ **15.** The librarian searched several databases before she found the answer to Colleen's question.

_____ **16.** The frustrated two-year-old scowled, turned red in the face, and finally let out an ear-piercing wail.

_____ **17.** The soccer player, sidelined by a torn ligament, watched his team score the winning goal.

_____ **18.** Elected by a large margin, the politician declared that she would fulfill all of her promises.

_____ **19.** Vicky sneezed, coughed, and blew her nose frequently when she suffered an allergy attack.

_____ **20.** Overwhelmed by a crush of hungry diners, the restaurant owner admitted that there could be too much of a good thing.

_____ **21.** The enraged steer bellowed, lowered its head, and charged at the rancher.

_____ **22.** Accompanied by John on drums, Luther on bass, and Travis on guitar, Kenny played a flawless trumpet solo.

_____ **23.** The electrical transformer, struck by lightning, exploded in a ball of fire.

_____ **24.** Grandmother's lined face reflected a lifetime of smiles, laughter, and love.

_____ **25.** The pierced tin lantern cast a beautiful pattern of light over the patio.

LANGUAGE HANDBOOK **6** **PHRASES**

WORKSHEET 5 | **Identifying and Using Gerunds and Gerund Phrases (Rules 6 g, h)**

EXERCISE A Underline each gerund or gerund phrase in the following sentences. If a sentence does not contain a gerund or a gerund phrase, write *NONE* on the line provided.

> **EXAMPLES** _____ 1. I like <u>listening to music with my friends</u>.
>
> __*NONE*__ 2. We were listening to music in the car.

_____ 1. Last week my friend Ravi was playing the *Graceland* CD, on which Paul Simon is accompanied by several well-known African musicians.

_____ 2. Listening to this amazing recording made me want to find out more about African music.

_____ 3. By doing a little research at the library, I discovered some interesting facts.

_____ 4. Holding an important role in African societies, music is a medium for the transmission of knowledge.

_____ 5. Another common purpose of music in Africa is celebrating community and personal events.

_____ 6. Singing is a significant part of most African people's lives.

_____ 7. Africans usually highlight important stages of their lives by making music.

_____ 8. People in many African societies participate in musical events by adding a voice or a clap pattern to a song's chorus.

_____ 9. In Ghana one can hear the performing of special songs when a child loses his or her first tooth.

_____ 10. Some men in Liberia use group singing in their work to coordinate their machete blows in clearing thick brush for rice fields.

EXERCISE B Underline each gerund or gerund phrase in the following sentences. On the line provided, identify its use in the sentence as *S* for subject, *PN* for predicate nominative, *DO* for direct object, or *OP* for object of a preposition. If a sentence does not contain a gerund or a gerund phrase, write *NONE*.

> **EXAMPLES** ___*OP*___ 1. Marla saved the puppy from <u>drowning</u>.
>
> ___*NONE*___ 2. Swinging hard, Mark McGwire hit the ball.

_____ 1. Did you hear that screeching owl at nightfall?

_____ 2. Mr. Garza heard low chanting in the courtyard.

_____ 3. Aunt Ramona's expertise is repairing the wicker on chairs.

_____ 4. Living in San Diego allows Andrea to stay close to her family.

_____ 5. By studying for four hours, Clarissa prepared for the exam.

LANGUAGE HANDBOOK 6 PHRASES

WORKSHEET 6 Identifying and Using Infinitives and Infinitive Phrases (Rules 6 i, j)

EXERCISE A Underline each infinitive or infinitive phrase in the following sentences. If a sentence does not contain an infinitive or an infinitive phrase, write *NONE* on the line provided.

EXAMPLES _____ **1.** Roger needs <u>to listen more closely to instructions</u>.

_____*NONE*_____ **2.** Vida went to Spain on her vacation.

_____ **1.** Hans has an assignment to complete for tomorrow.

_____ **2.** Yves likes to listen to Tonya reading poetry.

_____ **3.** Mr. McIntyre has the patience to play with his grandson all day.

_____ **4.** To get to the theater on time, Wendy and Zora left thirty minutes before the start of the performance.

_____ **5.** My little cousin Charlie's favorite activity is going to the grocery store.

EXERCISE B Underline each infinitive or infinitive phrase in the following sentences. On the line provided, identify its use in the sentence as *N* for noun, *ADJ* for adjective, or *ADV* for adverb. If a sentence does not contain an infinitive or an infinitive phrase, write *NONE*.

EXAMPLES _____*N*_____ **1.** Would you like <u>to participate in sled dog racing</u>?

_____*NONE*_____ **2.** Have you ever traveled to Alaska?

_____ **1.** Susan Butcher likes to compete in sled dog racing.

_____ **2.** She has managed to win the Iditarod Trail Sled Dog Race four times.

_____ **3.** In 1972, she moved to Colorado to become involved in sled dog racing, or mushing.

_____ **4.** In 1975, she moved to Alaska to train a dog team.

_____ **5.** To race in the Iditarod was her dream, which became a reality three years later.

_____ **6.** Another dream of hers was to lead a sled dog team to the summit of Mount McKinley for the first time.

_____ **7.** Susan Butcher was able to accomplish that dream.

_____ **8.** In 1985, she needed to withdraw her team from the Iditarod because of a moose attack.

_____ **9.** In 1986, she finally placed first, being the second woman to win the race.

_____ **10.** To win the famous race even once is difficult, but Susan Butcher won it for the fourth time in 1990.

| WORKSHEET 7 | **Identifying and Using Appositives and Appositive Phrases (Rules 6 k, l)** |

EXERCISE A   Underline each appositive or appositive phrase in the following sentences. A sentence may contain more than one appositive or appositive phrase. If a sentence does not contain an appositive or an appositive phrase, write *NONE* on the line provided.

EXAMPLES _____ **1.** The Kelly twins, <u>Rory</u> and <u>Rick</u>, are both excellent lacrosse players.

NONE **2.** The writer who is known as Mark Twain wrote a book titled *Life on the Mississippi*.

_____ **1.** Nowadays a lathe, a machine tool used for cutting metal or wood, is likely to be programmed by a computer.

_____ **2.** Quechua, the language of the Incas, is still spoken in South America.

_____ **3.** The composer George Gershwin wrote the music for the opera *Porgy and Bess*.

_____ **4.** Hosni owns books by Isaac Asimov, a scientist and science fiction writer.

_____ **5.** Ms. MacLeod, born in 1922 in Scotland, emigrated to Canada in 1928.

EXERCISE B   Underline each appositive or appositive phrase in the following sentences. Then, circle the word or words each appositive or appositive phrase explains or identifies.

EXAMPLE **1.** (June 21), the summer solstice, is Marguerite's birthday.

1. High-definition television, HDTV, has cinema-quality images.

2. Seneca, the Roman philosopher and statesman, was actually born in Córdoba, Spain.

3. A four-time recipient of the Pulitzer Prize for poetry, Robert Frost was the first poet to read a poem at a presidential inauguration.

4. French and Spanish, both Romance languages, share many similar words.

5. Several works by Caravaggio, Sandra's favorite painter, are on display at the museum.

6. Two crops, corn and potatoes, were grown in North and South America long before Europeans arrived.

7. When Akiho made a trip to Japan, he spent time in three cities, Osaka, Kyoto, and Nagasaki.

8. Lucy Telotte, Robert's cousin, grew up in Guam.

9. *Canis familiaris,* the domestic dog, has lived with humans since the days of the cave dwellers.

10. My friend Ingrid wrote to the Costa Rican consulate for information about tours.

WORKSHEET 8 Test (Rules 6 a–l)

EXERCISE A   Underline each prepositional phrase. Then, draw an arrow to the word or words that the phrase modifies. There may be more than one prepositional phrase in a sentence.

EXAMPLE   1. Mason drove his uncle <u>to the grocery store</u>.

1. Little droplets of rain were still falling outside the house.

2. When the game was over, the winning team came from the locker room and went to their bus.

3. The road around the lake was flooded after the heavy rains.

4. The novel *Sounder* tells about a boy and his dog.

5. What was the name of the dog in the novel?

6. Did you find the bag of rice in the cupboard or in the pantry?

7. Please bring the packages from the car and set them on the kitchen table.

8. Over the trees we saw a beautiful rainbow.

9. Have you ever read anything by the author Langston Hughes?

10. Our neighbors up the hill are also good friends of ours.

EXERCISE B   Underline the participle or participial phrase in each of the following sentences. Then, on the line provided, write the word that the participle or participial phrase modifies.

EXAMPLE   ___*baseball*___   1. The baseball, <u>signed by the entire team</u>, was my mother's most valuable possession.

_____   1. My dog wore a newly purchased collar.

_____   2. It will take more than a smiling face to impress the judges in the debate tournament.

_____   3. Trained technicians prepared the space shuttle for liftoff.

_____   4. Hey! Can you see the cat stalking the bird in the back yard?

_____   5. One of the most recommended features of the coat is its warm lining.

_____   6. Going through her backpack, Moira can't remember where she put her binoculars.

_____   7. Did you see that picture of my younger sister wearing a wool cap?

Continued ☞

_____ **8.** On Easter Island, strikingly carved statues are set up on stone platforms.

_____ **9.** In the ski lodge, we were warmed by the fire burning in the large fireplace.

_____ **10.** The hurricane, fed by cool wind currents and warm sea water, headed for the coast of Florida.

EXERCISE C   Underline each gerund or gerund phrase in the following sentences. Then, on the line provided, identify how the gerund or gerund phrase is being used by writing *S* for subject, *DO* for direct object, *OP* for object of a preposition, or *PN* for predicate nominative.

EXAMPLE _____S_____ **1.** <u>Sleeping</u> occupies much of a cat's day.

_____ **1.** Piloting twin-rotor helicopters takes special skills.

_____ **2.** My grandfather likes watching travel videos.

_____ **3.** Dr. Martin Luther King, Jr., was devoted to winning civil rights for African Americans.

_____ **4.** On your vacation, will you practice your windsurfing?

_____ **5.** The senator's thinking on the issues was clarified by years of study.

_____ **6.** One of the most impressive feats of ancient times was constructing Stonehenge.

_____ **7.** Michelle Kwan's most famous talent is ice-skating.

_____ **8.** You might consider keeping pigeons as a hobby.

_____ **9.** Somehow the rumbling of the railroad car helped me to sleep.

_____ **10.** Revealing the ending of the book would not be a very nice thing to do.

EXERCISE D   Underline the infinitive or infinitive phrase in each of the following sentences. Then, on the line provided, write *N* if the infinitive or infinitive phrase is used as a noun, *ADJ* if it is used as an adjective, or *ADV* if it is used as an adverb.

EXAMPLE _____ADV_____ **1.** Ms. Tanaka was careful <u>to include the entire class</u> in the discussion.

_____ **1.** Even though the concert doesn't start until 8:30 P.M., the members of the band need to be there early.

_____ **2.** The firefighter was courageous to have rescued the cat from the burning house.

_____ **3.** To fill the swimming pool, Paul turned the water on full blast.

Continued ☞

_____ **4.** You want to boil the water before putting in the pasta.

_____ **5.** To sing the role of Mimi in *La Bohème* at the Metropolitan Opera is the dream of every soprano.

_____ **6.** The best person to decorate the gym for the dance is Cordelia.

_____ **7.** Ross decided to ride his bicycle to the farmer's market.

_____ **8.** My mother's marketing company is searching for someone to write their advertisements for them.

_____ **9.** Aren't you curious to hear the result of the composer's revisions to the concerto?

_____ **10.** The running back surged ahead of the other team to score a touchdown.

EXERCISE E   Underline the appositive or appositive phrase in each of the following sentences. Then, on the line provided, write the word or words that the appositive or appositive phrase identifies or explains.

EXAMPLE   *T. E. Lawrence*   **1.** The British soldier T. E. Lawrence is the subject of a famous film.

_____ **1.** Both Tony and Patrice thought that the dog, a Labrador retriever, was very handsome.

_____ **2.** The highlight of the air show was the flight of a B-52, a jet bomber.

_____ **3.** Our reading group finally decided to read the last book on the list, *Moby-Dick*.

_____ **4.** The happiest moment in the movie was the unexpected return of the cat Thomasina.

_____ **5.** The Colossus of Rhodes, one of the Seven Wonders of the Ancient World, was said to stand over the harbor at Rhodes.

_____ **6.** Let me tell you about my grandfather, a Lakota medicine man.

_____ **7.** Our science teacher reproduced a famous experiment by Galileo Galilei, the Italian astronomer.

_____ **8.** My older brother Mike works on a television show in Los Angeles.

_____ **9.** Every Passover my family holds a Seder, a feast to celebrate the flight of the Jews from slavery in Egypt.

_____ **10.** In English class, we read a novel by Toni Morrison, a Nobel Prize–winning author.

| WORSHEET 1 | **Identifying Independent and Subordinate Clauses (Rules 7 a–c)** |

EXERCISE A   On the line provided, identify each of the following groups of words as *IND* for independent clause or *SUB* for subordinate clause. Put a capital letter at the beginning of each independent clause and a period at the end.

EXAMPLES ___IND___ **1.** It has been an exciting week for us.

___SUB___ **2.** when we opened the door

_____ **1.** today Rosa celebrates her birthday

_____ **2.** after we found the boat on the lake shore

_____ **3.** on the bow it had the name *Limber Lost*

_____ **4.** he has been to the Crow Indian Reservation in Montana

_____ **5.** until we read poems by Rita Dove

_____ **6.** reluctantly Dan offered to take it back

_____ **7.** that Toshiro helped

_____ **8.** whom they saw coming across the street

_____ **9.** we will save the ten-dollar reward to buy our own canoe

_____ **10.** which we saw in the mail-order catalog

EXERCISE B   Underline the ten subordinate clauses in the following paragraph. Not every sentence has a subordinate clause. If a sentence does not contain a subordinate clause, write *NONE* above the sentence.

EXAMPLE   [1] Yesterday Suni earned money to help the flood victims <u>whom she heard about on TV</u>.

[1] After the rain stopped, Suni noticed many cars that she thought were very dirty. [2] She stopped at each house where a dirty car was parked out front. [3] Because she is a good salesperson, several of the people whom she approached were glad to have her wash their cars. [4] At one house, the family's three children helped as she washed their station wagon. [5] She charged three dollars for every car that she washed and waxed. [6] Today she is stiff and sore from her work. [7] She donated the money that she earned to the Red Cross, which distributes funds to flood victims. [8] That her money is going toward a good cause makes Suni happy.

LANGUAGE HANDBOOK **7** CLAUSES

WORKSHEET 2 Identifying and Using Adjective Clauses (Rule 7 d)

EXERCISE A Underline the adjective clause in each of the following sentences, and underline twice the word the clause modifies.

> **EXAMPLE 1.** My friend Coretta is a <u>painter</u> <u>whose hero is Jacob Lawrence</u>.

1. She showed me Lawrence's *Harriet Tubman* series, which includes thirty-one paintings.

2. Many of Lawrence's paintings tell about persons who underwent incredible struggles.

3. The paintings reflect scenes of African American life that may have been overlooked.

4. Lawrence's techniques, which include bold images and vivid colors, communicate strong emotion.

5. Tubman, who was a former slave, became an organizer of the Underground Railroad.

6. Scenes from Tubman's life, which show both slavery and freedom, tell a powerful story.

7. Violent images that reflect slavery contrast with images showing quiet strength and purpose.

8. Lawrence, whose paintings were probably influenced by others' descriptions, portrays Tubman as fierce.

9. One painting includes a caption that advertises a reward for Tubman's capture.

10. The last pictures in the series show the Civil War, which brought an end to slavery.

EXERCISE B Combine each of the following pairs of sentences by changing the italicized sentence to an adjective clause. Use the relative pronoun shown in parentheses. Place each clause immediately after the word it modifies, and insert commas where necessary.

> **EXAMPLE 1.** I am wearing a new sweater. *Louisa made it for me.* (that)
> <u>I am wearing a new sweater that Louisa made for me.</u>

1. We read <u>The Autobiography of Miss Jane Pittman</u>. *It is about an African American woman reflecting on her life.* (which) _____

_____

_____

2. Ronald has a new car. *It has air conditioning.* (that) _____

_____

_____

Continued ☞

3. Mrs. Olson contributed some canned food for our food drive. *She owns a grocery store on Park Street.* (who) _____

_____

_____

4. Here is an Ernesto Galarza story. *I found it in a book in my grandparents' attic.* (that)

_____

_____

5. Yolanda is the star of our musical. *Her voice is lovely.* (whose) _____

_____

_____

EXERCISE C   Fill in the blank in each of the following sentences with an appropriate relative pronoun.

> EXAMPLE **1.** Gary Soto studied the work of Federico García Lorca and Pablo Neruda, _____*who*_____ are famous Latin American poets.

1. Much of the farm labor in the San Joaquin valley in central California is done by people _____ are migrant workers.

2. The clown costume _____ Jeff made from scratch is wonderful.

3. We looked at Jeremy, toward _____ Mr. Acoli was pointing.

4. Marci, _____ ambition is to be a forest ranger, spends her summers as a lookout in a national park.

5. Crater Lake attracts many tourists, _____ go to see the deep blue color of the lake.

6. The giant sequoia trees _____ grow in California and Oregon are probably the largest trees in the world.

7. John Henry is a legendary African American laborer _____ worked on the Chesapeake and Ohio Railroad.

8. Lori, with _____ we traveled, took many pictures.

9. The passenger pigeon, _____ was once abundant, is now extinct.

10. Mercury, _____ is one of the smallest planets in our solar system, has craters like those on the moon.

Elements of Literature

LANGUAGE
HANDBOOK **7** CLAUSES

| WORKSHEET 3 | Identifying and Using Adverb Clauses (Rule 7 e)

EXERCISE A   In the following sentences, underline each adverb clause and circle the subordinating conjunction.

> EXAMPLE 1. Ricardo and Maria started swimming lessons (after) they
> moved near the athletic club.

1. They chose this sport because they can practice it year-round.

2. They like to swim for an hour before they go to school.

3. Maria concentrates on the backstroke so that she can be the best in that event.

4. Ricardo likes the butterfly stroke, since it develops his shoulder and arm muscles.

5. The swimmers compete in meets whenever they are held in the area.

6. If they practice, Ricardo and Maria will be able to compete better.

7. Maria and Ricardo time themselves on each lap as they practice.

8. They analyze their performance after each meet is over.

9. Although swimming is usually an individual sport, Ricardo and Maria also swim on relay teams with other club members.

10. As soon as Maria's younger sister is old enough to compete, she will also swim on a relay team.

EXERCISE B   Combine each of the following pairs of sentences into one sentence by changing the italicized sentence to an adverb clause. Use the conjunction in parentheses to begin the clause. You can place the clause at the beginning or the end of the sentence. Be sure to use a comma if the clause is at the beginning of the sentence.

> EXAMPLE 1. Dad called. *You were at the store.* (while) _Dad called_
> _while you were at the store._ **or** _While you were at the store,_
> _Dad called._

1. *Mother's birthday is tomorrow.* Luis is going to prepare a special dinner. (because)

_____

_____

2. Amy prepared the salad. *We stripped the husks off the corn.* (while) _____

_____

_____

Continued ☞

3. I can't go to the game. *I must finish my science notebook.* (since) _____

_____

_____

4. *My pen ran out of ink.* I finished my outline in pencil. (after) _____

_____

_____

5. I worried about the history test. *I knew I was going to do well.* (although) _____

_____

_____

6. *We were hunting for project material.* We found three articles on the Battle of
Wounded Knee. (when) _____

_____

_____

7. *Jill was the smallest girl on her team.* She was the best player. (although) _____

_____

_____

8. *Brian has overslept.* He will be late for school. (since) _____

_____

_____

9. We gave up our picnic plans. *The rain was beginning to fall.* (because) _____

_____

_____

10. *Mom and Dad had left for the political caucus.* Lisa and I began our homework. (after)

_____

_____

LANGUAGE
HANDBOOK **7** CLAUSES

WORKSHEET 4 Identifying Noun Clauses (Rule 7 f)

EXERCISE A   Underline each noun clause in the following sentences.

> **EXAMPLE 1.** <u>That Mr. Ippolito wants to encourage volunteerism among his students</u> is obvious.

1. Mr. Ippolito asked our eighth-grade class what we would like to do as a community volunteer project.

2. Volunteer work gives whoever does it a terrific feeling of accomplishment.

3. That we give help to more than one person seemed like a good idea to Lee Anne.

4. "Cleaning up Founders Park is what really needs to be done," suggested Lacreesha.

5. Since more than half the students agreed with what Lacreesha had suggested, Mr. Ippolito's class cleaned Founders Park the following Saturday.

EXERCISE B   Underline each noun clause in the following sentences. On the line provided, identify it as *S* for subject, *PN* for predicate nominative, *DO* for direct object, *IO* for indirect object, or *OP* for object of a preposition. If a sentence does not contain a noun clause, write *NONE*.

> **EXAMPLE**   ___*OP*___ **1.** I can talk about basketball all day to <u>whoever will listen to me</u>.

_____ **1.** Whoever knows me is aware of my love of basketball.

_____ **2.** I give my complete attention to whatever game is on TV at the moment.

_____ **3.** Learning facts about the players is what fascinates me the most.

_____ **4.** Hakeem Olajuwon, who was born in Nigeria, is considered one of the greatest centers in the National Basketball Association (NBA).

_____ **5.** That Olajuwon was voted NBA Defensive Player of the Year in 1994 came as no surprise to me.

_____ **6.** He was recognized for what he does best: blocking shots, rebounding, and scoring.

_____ **7.** Did you know that Olajuwon wrote an autobiography, *Living the Dream: My Life and Basketball*?

_____ **8.** Kareem Abdul-Jabbar is another player who gave whoever watched him on the court an exciting display of his skills.

_____ **9.** That Abdul-Jabbar led the Los Angeles Lakers to five NBA championships is proof of his abilities.

_____ **10.** A little-known fact about Abdul-Jabbar is that he changed his name from Lew Alcindor in 1971.

WORKSHEET 5 | Test (Rules 7 a–f)

EXERCISE A   On the line provided, identify the italicized clause in each sentence as
IND for independent clause or *SUB* for subordinate clause.

EXAMPLES   __SUB__   **1.** Can you name an athlete *who recently broke
a world record*?

__IND__   **2.** *Ashley and I volunteered to help with*
whatever needed doing.

_____ **1.** One of the students asked *who wrote the poem "Stopping by Woods on a
Snowy Evening."*

_____ **2.** Before the last bell had sounded, *all the students were in their seats and
ready to work.*

_____ **3.** My mother, *who loves to dance,* showed us how to do the samba.

_____ **4.** After the sun went down, *the music drifted on the night air.*

_____ **5.** We can eat at *whichever restaurant you prefer.*

_____ **6.** While the Lerners were away, *we took care of their pets.*

_____ **7.** All the dogs in the kennel began barking, and my father went to see *what
was bothering them.*

_____ **8.** Mr. Kurosawa showed us a samurai sword *that had belonged to his
grandfather.*

_____ **9.** *Luisa's uncle left early for the train station* so that he could arrive on
time.

_____ **10.** Sarah could not remember *where she had left her glasses.*

EXERCISE B   Underline the adjective clause in each of the following sentences.
Underline twice the relative pronoun that signals the beginning of the adjective clause.

EXAMPLE **1.** Alberto met Maya Lin, <u>who designed the Vietnam Veterans
Memorial in Washington, D.C.</u>

1. Ricardo plays jai alai, which is a popular Basque handball game.

2. Dorothy Sayers was a scholar and teacher who also wrote detective stories.

3. The cat with the white ears is the one that I want.

4. Here is the music that we are playing in the Thanksgiving program.

5. Andrea is the student whose photographs are on display.

6. The cello is an instrument that Yo-Yo Ma has played since the age of four.

Continued ☞

7. Mary Shelley, whom many remember as the author of *Frankenstein,* was also the wife of the poet Percy Bysshe Shelley.

8. Gold and platinum are two metals that are often used in electronic components.

9. Many of the people who headed for California during the gold rush were quite ignorant about life there.

10. Our car, which was in an accident, is being repaired.

EXERCISE C Underline the adverb clause in each of the following sentences, and circle the subordinating conjunction at the beginning of the clause.

> **EXAMPLE 1.** Life has been very different in my family (since) Mother passed her bar exam.

1. Because she works long hours at her new office, we all have additional tasks around the house.

2. Father now does most of the cooking, since he comes home first.

3. Although he had cooked at cookouts and on Sunday mornings, he had never before planned a weekly menu.

4. He is quite a good cook because he is willing to experiment.

5. He has prepared several unusual dishes because he finds them tasty.

6. Father became familiar with many Southeast Asian foods when he was a foreign correspondent in Thailand.

7. If Mother, Father, and I all pitch in and clean up after dinner, the job gets done much quicker.

8. Actually, we have all grown closer since Mother started her job.

9. We usually play a board game together after we have cleaned up from dinner.

10. Mother and Father are saving part of their salaries so that we can take a trip to South America this summer.

LANGUAGE HANDBOOK **8** SENTENCES

WORKSHEET 1

Identifying Sentences and Sentence Fragments
(Rule 8 a)

EXERCISE   Write *S* before each group of words that is a sentence. Capitalize the first letter and add end punctuation. Write *F* before each group of words that is a fragment.

EXAMPLES   ___S___   **1.** *F* fishing is Kevin's favorite hobby**.**

___F___   **2.** especially in salt water

_____   **1.** because so many different kinds of fish

_____   **2.** Kevin has several rods and reels

_____   **3.** the bluefish start running in the late summer

_____   **4.** traveling in schools and feeding greedily

_____   **5.** they require big hooks and a strong fishing rod

_____   **6.** striped bass also good to eat

_____   **7.** they breed in freshwater rivers

_____   **8.** return to the ocean during adulthood

_____   **9.** also big tuna off Block Island

_____   **10.** don't party boats take many people to the fishing grounds

_____   **11.** flounder can be found in coves

_____   **12.** pull your hook up a couple of inches from the bottom

_____   **13.** excellent to pan-fry for supper

_____   **14.** are all fish good to eat

_____   **15.** menhaden are caught for fertilizer

_____   **16.** a sea trout caught off the end of the pier

_____   **17.** out in the rowboat at dawn

_____   **18.** sandworms make very good bait

_____   **19.** a funny-looking fish is the sea robin

_____   **20.** it swells up to twice its size when caught

_____   **21.** is it designed to frighten its enemies

_____   **22.** a good scaling knife and a board to put the fish on

_____   **23.** one time Kevin caught an eel

_____   **24.** threw it back into the water

_____   **25.** nothing better than good, fresh fish

NAME _____ CLASS _____ DATE _____

WORKSHEET 2 | Correcting Sentence Fragments (Rule 8 a)

EXERCISE   Each of the numbered items below consists of two groups of words. If both groups are sentences, write *S* on the line provided. If one is a sentence fragment, write *F* and combine the fragment with the sentence. Cross out each incorrect capital letter, and write the lowercase letter above it. Cross out the incorrect periods, and add commas where they are needed.

EXAMPLES ___F___ **1.** The Cherokee are an American Indian people./Who once lived in what is now the southeastern United States.

___S___ **2.** The land that is now Georgia was originally inhabited by the Cherokee. They were a southern branch of the Iroquois.

_____ **1.** The Cherokee constructed their towns in fortified places in the mountains. So that they could live in peace, isolated from aggressive neighbors.

_____ **2.** When the settlers moved into their lands. The Cherokee tried to adapt to the new culture.

_____ **3.** Under the leadership of Chief Sequoyah, they drew up a constitution for their nation. Following the example of the settlers.

_____ **4.** Many of the new settlers did not want to live side by side with the Cherokee. Whom they considered a conquered nation.

_____ **5.** In 1802, the federal government, promising land in the Great Plains, agreed. To move the Cherokee from Georgia.

_____ **6.** The Cherokee tried to obtain justice. And brought suit against Georgia in a case called *Cherokee Nation* v. *Georgia,* 1831.

_____ **7.** Finally, the Supreme Court was forced to take the case. It upheld the rights of the Cherokee.

_____ **8.** It seemed like a victory, but President Andrew Jackson refused. To intervene when Georgia denied the Cherokee their rights.

_____ **9.** The Cherokee were forced to leave their ancestral home. In favor of lands promised them in the Great Plains.

_____ **10.** Many suffered and died during the journey to the new territory. The forced march of the Cherokee came to be known as the Trail of Tears.

LANGUAGE HANDBOOK 8 SENTENCES

WORSHEET 3 | **Identifying the Complete Subject and the Complete Predicate (Rule 8 b)**

EXERCISE In the following sentences, underline the complete subject once and the complete predicate twice.

> **EXAMPLE 1.** <u>As a child, did</u> <u>you</u> <u>like to draw fabulous creatures</u>?

1. Maritza's favorite things to draw are imaginary creatures.

2. She and her friends spend hours inventing beasts.

3. Then they vote for the most imaginative creature among the group.

4. Can you guess Maritza's favorite fabulous creature?

5. It is the legendary monster called the griffin.

6. The griffin is a combination of species.

7. Having the head, beak, and wings of an eagle and the body and legs of a lion, the griffin represents strength and vigilance.

8. The griffin originated in the Middle East.

9. Pictures of it were found in the artwork of the ancient Babylonians and Assyrians.

10. The ancient Romans also created images of the griffin.

11. The griffin also appeared in medieval books.

12. During the Middle Ages, griffins sometimes served as gargoyles in Gothic architecture.

13. Maritza's best friend, Susannah, prefers to draw dragons.

14. The dragon symbolizes destruction, death, and evil in some belief systems.

15. Included in this group are the Mesopotamian, Hebrew, and Christian belief systems.

16. In the English epic *Beowulf,* the old hero slays a dragon but loses his own life.

17. Doesn't the legend of Saint George, the patron saint of England, describe his killing a dragon and rescuing a princess?

18. However, in some mythologies the dragon has beneficial powers.

19. According to the ancient Greeks and Romans, dragons could understand and reveal to humans the secrets of the earth.

20. Among the Celts, the dragon symbolized supreme political authority.

21. Later, the legendary creature appeared on the battle flags of English kings.

22. In Chinese mythology the dragon is a symbol of good fortune.

23. Parades in China on New Year's Day often feature a group of people wearing a long dragon costume.

24. This mock dragon is said to prevent misfortune in the new year.

25. In Chinese farming communities, some people credit dragons with controlling the rainfall and affecting the harvest.

LANGUAGE
HANDBOOK **8** SENTENCES

WORKSHEET 4 | **Identifying the Simple Subject and the Simple Predicate (Rules 8 b–d)**

EXERCISE A   In each of the following sentences, draw a vertical line between the complete subject and the complete predicate. Then, underline the simple subject once and the simple predicate twice. Be sure to include helping verbs.

> EXAMPLE **1.** Our <u>trip</u> to Chile | <u>had</u> already <u>begun</u> at the airport.

1. We were eager to see the land so beautifully described by Pablo Neruda.

2. Our reservations on the flight were quickly confirmed at the desk.

3. The flight attendant welcomed all the passengers aboard the plane.

4. The engines roared to life a few minutes later.

5. All the people on board had by then fastened their seat belts.

6. The takeoff was for me the most exciting part of the flight.

7. Captain Garcia introduced herself over the intercom.

8. She told us the altitude and speed of the airplane.

9. A dinner was served on plastic trays.

10. Our flight to Chile took ten hours.

EXERCISE B   Write the simple subject and simple predicate of each of the following sentences on the lines provided. If the subject is the understood *you,* write *you* on the line provided.

> **Subject Predicate**
> EXAMPLE ___*cat*___ ___*is named*___ **1.** My cat is named Tiger Lily.

Subject   Predicate

_____ _____ 1. Harriet Tubman risked her life to help slaves escape the South.

_____ _____ 2. Approximately 200,000 people marched in Washington, D.C., on August 28, 1963, to hear Martin Luther King, Jr., speak.

_____ _____ 3. The fox streaked across the meadow.

_____ _____ 4. The lion on the savanna looks fierce.

_____ _____ 5. Everyone in our neighborhood has signed the petition.

_____ _____ 6. We do not always copy instructions accurately enough.

_____ _____ 7. Don't forget to bring your book.

_____ _____ 8. Have you read the poem by Langston Hughes?

_____ _____ 9. One of us should help him.

_____ _____ 10. Our junior high school dance will be held next Friday night.

WORSHEET 5	**Identifying and Using Compound Subjects and Compound Verbs (Rules 8 e, f)**

EXERCISE A   In the following sentences, underline the simple subject once and the verb twice. Remember to underline all parts of a compound subject or a compound verb.

> EXAMPLE **1.** The Greek <u>gods</u> <u>punished</u> mortals but often <u>left</u> them hope.

1. Pandora received a sealed box from the gods and was curious about its contents.

2. She had been warned against opening the box but opened it anyway.

3. Despair and Disease flew out of the box and frightened Pandora.

4. Plague and Sorrow followed shortly after.

5. At last, Hope remained in the box and gave comfort to Pandora.

6. Io also suffered a horrible fate but was given hope for a brighter future.

7. Zeus loved her and unintentionally caused her misfortune.

8. She was turned into a calf and was pursued by a biting fly.

9. Peace and rest finally came to her in Egypt.

10. She was turned back into a woman and had a child named Epaphus.

EXERCISE B   Fill in the blanks with compound subjects and verbs that make sense.

> EXAMPLE **1.** Carlos ____*reads*____ and ____*enjoys*____ mystery stories.

1. _____ and _____ like stories by Sandra Cisneros.

2. Angelo carefully _____ the tomato plants and _____ the stems to the stakes.

3. _____ or _____ would make a good class president.

4. The old judge _____ sympathetically but _____ the prisoner back to jail.

5. _____ and _____ are my favorite hobbies.

6. _____ and _____ are two presidents I admire.

7. On the first spring day we always _____ to the park and _____ a few games of baseball.

8. Neither _____ nor _____ has been able to decide on a name for his puppy.

9. The blues is a style of music first developed in the rural South by African Americans that has since _____ and _____ all over the world.

10. _____ and _____ are two books that I have enjoyed recently.

WORKSHEET 6 Test (Rules 8 a–f)

EXERCISE A On the line provided for each of the following groups of words, write *S* if the word group is a sentence, and add end punctuation. Write *F* before each group that is a fragment.

EXAMPLES ____*F*____ 1. Which is part of the Himalayas

____*S*____ 2. Mount Everest is still a great challenge for climbers.

_____ 1. The summit of Mount Everest in the Himalayas is the highest point on earth

_____ 2. Because Tenzing Norgay had always wanted to climb Mount Everest

_____ 3. Tenzing devoted his life to his dream of reaching the top of the great mountain

_____ 4. In May 1953, while Tenzing was on an expedition with some British climbers

_____ 5. Did Tenzing and Edmund P. Hillary make up one of the climbing teams

_____ 6. Which they succeeded in reaching on May 29, 1953

_____ 7. This unknown Sherpa guide who started the dangerous climb with Hillary

_____ 8. After his successful climb had made him famous

_____ 9. Because his people have no written language, Tenzing could not write his own story

_____ 10. James Ullman talked with Tenzing and wrote *Tiger of the Snows* for him

EXERCISE B Attach the sentence fragments in the paragraph below to the sentences with which they belong. Cross out the incorrect periods, and add commas where needed. Cross out each incorrect capital letter, and write the correct lowercase letter above it.

EXAMPLE The current American flag has fifty stars./And thirteen stripes.

Today, there are still only thirteen stripes in the American flag, but there might have been fifty. If Congress had not changed its mind. On January 1, 1776, General Washington flew the first flag of the United States. The Grand Union flag. It had the flag of Great Britain in its corner and a stripe. For each of the original thirteen colonies. In 1777, Congress changed the flag. By adding a blue field with thirteen stars. As new states entered the Union. Stars and stripes were added until, in 1818, Congress restored the original thirteen stripes.

Continued ☞

EXERCISE C In each of the following sentences, draw a vertical line to separate the subject from the predicate.

> EXAMPLE **1.** The choice of a career | is an important decision.

1. Cesar Chavez organized Californian farm workers in the 1960s.

2. One of his achievements was a boycott of California grapes.

3. My friend Sharon wants to be a meteorologist.

4. We must soon consider the problem of global warming seriously.

5. Our high school courses will affect our future jobs.

6. Some of my friends will take vocational courses.

7. Other boys and girls will prepare for college.

8. I have not decided yet.

9. One of my cousins has just started graduate school.

10. He is studying the founding of the La Raza Unida Party in 1970.

EXERCISE D In the following sentences, underline the complete subject once and the complete predicate twice.

> EXAMPLE **1.** <u>Have you</u> <u>heard the term *Cajun* before</u>?

1. The first Cajuns moved to Louisiana from Canada.

2. Today, the Cajun community in southwestern Louisiana includes descendants of those immigrants.

3. In the late 1800s, many Cajun landowners were forced to sell their property.

4. Many Cajuns left Louisiana during the early part of the twentieth century.

5. They were attracted by the jobs in the new shipyards and refineries in eastern Texas.

6. The Cajuns remaining in Louisiana found their French language and culture under attack by the state government.

7. Until the 1960s, all public school classes in Louisiana had to be taught only in English.

8. In the late 1960s, young Cajun college students protested the suppression of their culture.

9. Finally, the Louisiana state legislature established the Council for the Development of French in Louisiana to help revive the Cajun culture.

10. Today Cajun music and foods are popular in many parts of the United States.

Continued ☞

EXERCISE E In each of the following sentences, underline the simple subject once and the simple predicate twice. Be sure to include all the parts of a verb phrase.

> EXAMPLE 1. Drought can occur during the summer months.

1. The farmers in our area are worrying about the drought.
2. No rain has fallen for sixty-two days.
3. Are the summer crops wilting in the fields?
4. Great cracks have formed in the clay of the riverbeds.
5. The sun creeps over a dusty horizon every morning.
6. Clouds have sometimes gathered in the sky.
7. They never turn into a storm.
8. The farmers are preparing for irrigation.
9. The disaster area must rely on federal aid.
10. All of us are hoping that it will rain soon.

EXERCISE F In each of the following sentences, underline the simple subject once and the simple predicate twice. If the subject is the understood *you*, write *you* on the line provided. Include all parts of a compound subject, a compound verb, or a verb phrase.

> EXAMPLES _____you_____ 1. Listen more and talk less.
>
> _____ 2. Marian and Judith wrote and directed a short film.

_____ 1. Ezra Pound and Maya Angelou are Beatrice's favorite American poets.

_____ 2. The planning committee researched several locations and wrote a report.

_____ 3. Does Melissa or Beto have the correct answer?

_____ 4. Please understand my dilemma.

_____ 5. One of Tran's explanations seems more logical than the other ones.

_____ 6. In your opinion, were the 1920s or the 1960s the more interesting decade in U.S. history?

_____ 7. Rigoberta Menchú Tum received the Nobel Peace Prize in 1992 and then returned to Guatemala to work for social change.

_____ 8. Under other circumstances, would you have chosen the red bicycle?

_____ 9. Why are there fewer frogs now than twenty years ago?

_____ 10. The musical *West Side Story* is based on Shakespeare's *Romeo and Juliet*.

LANGUAGE HANDBOOK **9** COMPLEMENTS

WORKSHEET 1 Identifying Subjects, Verbs, and Complements (Rule 9 a)

EXERCISE In the following sentences, underline each subject once, underline each verb twice, and circle each complement. A sentence may not have a complement, or it may have more than one complement.

EXAMPLE 1. <u>John Glenn</u> <u>is</u> a famous (American.)

1. John Glenn has been a test pilot, an astronaut, and a United States senator.

2. He has excelled in all three professions.

3. After graduating from high school, he attended Muskingum College in New Concord, Ohio.

4. He received a bachelor's degree in engineering.

5. In World War II, Glenn joined the Marine Corps.

6. As a Marine fighter pilot, he flew fifty-nine combat missions in the South Pacific.

7. He also piloted jet fighters in the Korean War.

8. During the 1950s, Glenn served in the Navy and the Marine Corps as a test pilot.

9. In July of 1957, he set a transcontinental speed record.

10. He piloted an F8U jet fighter from Los Angeles to New York in three hours and twenty-three minutes.

11. In 1959, the National Aeronautics and Space Administration selected Glenn and six other pilots as the first American astronauts.

12. Glenn and the other astronauts trained rigorously to prepare for their space flights.

13. On February 20, 1962, NASA gave Glenn the opportunity to be the first American to orbit the earth.

14. On board a Mercury space capsule, he made three orbits around the earth in five hours.

15. His capsule was called *Friendship 7*.

16. During the flight, the capsule reached a maximum altitude of 162 miles.

17. After leaving the space program, Glenn entered politics in 1970.

18. He was elected to the U.S. Senate from Ohio in 1974.

19. Glenn was a United States senator for four consecutive terms.

20. In 1998, NASA selected Glenn to fly in space one more time as a member of the crew of the space shuttle *Discovery*.

LANGUAGE HANDBOOK 9 COMPLEMENTS

WORKSHEET 2 | **Identifying Direct Objects (Rule 9 b)**

EXERCISE A   Underline the direct object in each of the following sentences.

> **EXAMPLE 1.** Our train left the <u>station</u>.

1. Muslims follow the teachings of Mohammed.

2. Our dog chased a squirrel out of our yard.

3. Mother likes carrot juice with her lunch.

4. Jamaica Kincaid published her first piece of fiction in *The New Yorker* in 1978.

5. Our family ate dinner at a restaurant yesterday.

6. Don washed his car on Thursday.

7. Maria wanted a catcher's mitt for her birthday.

8. We frequently visit Aunt Edith in Brooklyn.

9. We use the Arabic numeric system.

10. I have brought my CDs for the party.

EXERCISE B   In each of the following sentences, underline the verb once and the direct object twice, if there is one. If a sentence does not have a direct object, write *NONE* on the line provided.

> **EXAMPLES** _____ **1.** The Iroquois <u>had</u> a highly complex political <u>system</u>.
>
> ___*NONE*___ **2.** The Iroquois <u>were</u> an American Indian people.

_____ **1.** Some of the Iroquois family of nations settled in what is now New York State.

_____ **2.** Five of these peoples formed a league.

_____ **3.** They were the Mohawk, the Seneca, the Oneida, the Onondaga, and the Cayuga.

_____ **4.** Hiawatha helped in the creation of the league.

_____ **5.** With others, he also created some of its laws.

_____ **6.** The league honored Hiawatha.

_____ **7.** Henry Wadsworth Longfellow used the name of Hiawatha in a poem about a different people, the Ojibwas.

_____ **8.** In 1722, the Tuscaroras joined the league.

_____ **9.** The name of this league was the Six Nations.

_____ **10.** We still have some poems by the Iroquois.

LANGUAGE
HANDBOOK **9** **COMPLEMENTS**

| WORSHEET 3 | **Identifying Direct Objects and Indirect Objects (Rule 9 b–c)** |

EXERCISE In the following sentences, underline each direct object once and each indirect object twice. If a sentence does not contain a direct object, write *NONE* on the line provided.

EXAMPLES _____ 1. Please bring <u>me</u> a <u>dishcloth</u> from the kitchen.

*NONE* 2. The weather became very warm in May.

_____ 1. The science class watched a video about photosynthesis.

_____ 2. Ms. O'Donnell told her granddaughter several stories about Ireland.

_____ 3. The Rembrandt painting hangs on the far wall.

_____ 4. Is Ali bringing you the newspaper?

_____ 5. The young boy stayed quiet throughout the recital.

_____ 6. The salesperson gave us her business card.

_____ 7. The master of ceremonies presented the award to Barry.

_____ 8. My uncle Hershel remained a loyal Lakers fan his entire life.

_____ 9. Take Lawanda and Johnny this pumpkin bread.

_____ 10. Roxanne gave her best friend an Amy Grant CD on her birthday.

_____ 11. Misha, send your cousin a note and a few photographs.

_____ 12. Bruce Springsteen often sings songs about ordinary people.

_____ 13. Ms. Rizzo seems unusually thoughtful this evening.

_____ 14. We saw Venus in the eastern sky at dusk.

_____ 15. In a restaurant in Hollywood, Eddie saw a movie star across the room.

_____ 16. Who was the first person in orbit?

_____ 17. The Dalmatian's exceptional memory gives it value as a performing dog.

_____ 18. My friend Narciso is from the Navajo reservation in northeastern Arizona.

_____ 19. Aunt Margaret is leaving her porcelain china to Pamela and Todd.

_____ 20. In the last few seconds of the game, Kelly passed Rachel the ball.

_____ 21. Peter gave me his baseball, bat, and collection of baseball cards.

_____ 22. The writer Michael Ondaatje won the 1992 Booker Prize for his novel *The English Patient.*

_____ 23. Victoria polished the coffee table with special care.

_____ 24. The counselor gave Jacob and me some interesting advice.

_____ 25. Your aunt Cecilia has high expectations of you, Antonio.

LANGUAGE
HANDBOOK **9** COMPLEMENTS

WORKSHEET 4 Identifying Linking Verbs, Predicate Nominatives,
and Predicate Adjectives (Rules 9 d, e)

EXERCISE A   Underline each subject complement in the following sentences. On the
line provided, write *PN* if the complement is a predicate nominative and *PA* if the
complement is a predicate adjective. If there is no subject complement in the sentence,
write *NONE*.

EXAMPLES   __PN__   1. My grandmother is my favorite <u>relative</u>.

__NONE__   2. She has taught me many things.

_____   1. I learned to speak Hebrew from her.

_____   2. She was always a patient teacher.

_____   3. Often she gives good advice.

_____   4. She is the source of endless stories about her childhood.

_____   5. She escaped Nazi Germany with her family at age seven.

_____   6. Her family were together in Israel for many years.

_____   7. Once she was a reporter for a New York City newspaper.

_____   8. She still looks very beautiful.

_____   9. It is strange to think of all of the experiences she has had.

_____   10. My grandmother remembers many exciting incidents.

EXERCISE B   In each of the following sentences, underline the linking verb once
(including any helping verbs) and underline the subject complement twice. On the line
provided, write *PN* for predicate nominative if the complement is a noun or pronoun and
PA for predicate adjective if the complement is an adjective.

EXAMPLE   __PN__   1. Our new car <u>is</u> the small <u>one</u> in the driveway.

_____   1. Mario is always active in class discussions.

_____   2. This red sweater is the one I made.

_____   3. Rosa Gomez became a lawyer.

_____   4. The squirrels in the woods near our house seem tame.

_____   5. Kimchi tastes best when you prepare it yourself.

_____   6. The lake looks very calm in the moonlight.

_____   7. He will be a member of the marching band this year.

_____   8. Firefighters must remain calm in an emergency.

_____   9. Yesterday I felt hungry long before lunch period.

_____   10. The book in the store window is *A Tale of Two Cities*.

WORKSHEET 5 | Test (Rules 9 a–e)

EXERCISE A In the following sentences, underline each subject once, underline each verb twice, and circle each complement. A sentence may have more than one complement.

> EXAMPLE 1. C. S. Lewis was a (professor) at Cambridge University and the (author) of *The Chronicles of Narnia*.

1. My sister is the best first-base player on the team.

2. I gave her a baseball mitt for her birthday.

3. She was very happy with the new glove.

4. The clerk at the convenience store gave Anna and Edwin directions to the Alamodome.

5. Long-distance running improves Chester's endurance and concentration.

6. Stephanie showed us a picture of cats on surfboards.

7. That steep slope looks difficult even for an experienced runner.

8. Professor Achebe brought his class souvenirs from his trip to Rapa Nui.

9. *The Return of the King* is the third book in J.R.R. Tolkien's famous trilogy, *Lord of the Rings*.

10. Tolkien invented several languages for his characters to use, including Elvish.

EXERCISE B In the following sentences, underline each direct object once and each indirect object twice. If a sentence does not contain a direct object or an indirect object, write *NONE* on the line provided.

> EXAMPLES _____ 1. Freda gave the <u>dog</u> some <u>food</u>.
>
> _*NONE*_ 2. The dog was very hungry.

_____ 1. Our class read *The Red Badge of Courage*.

_____ 2. Please give your teacher this note.

_____ 3. The statue of the college's founder is across the park.

_____ 4. Did Tania buy you a bagel?

_____ 5. Mr. Wilton built his children a swing set in the back yard.

_____ 6. The obstacle course looks extremely difficult.

_____ 7. At the school assembly, the principal presented Jerome and Sandy with awards for perfect attendance.

Continued ☞

_____ 8. If you're going to the cafeteria, please bring me a sandwich and a glass of apple juice.

_____ 9. Peggy took the books back to the library.

_____ 10. My father gave Roberto and Tony a small loan and some good advice for their new business.

EXERCISE C   On the line provided, identify each complement in italics by writing *DO* for direct object, *IO* for indirect object, *PN* for predicate nominative, or *PA* for predicate adjective.

EXAMPLE ____PN____ 1. The viola is my favorite stringed *instrument.*

_____ 1. Given the circumstances, Julia is extremely *fortunate.*

_____ 2. Abraham Lincoln delivered the *Gettysburg Address* on November 19, 1863.

_____ 3. Why does Ms. Yakamoto look a little *sad* today?

_____ 4. Lorraine is the best *golfer* ever to attend Washington High School.

_____ 5. Please send your *mother* my greetings.

EXERCISE D   Underline each complement in the following sentences. Then, on the line provided, identify the complement as *DO* for direct object, *IO* for indirect object, *PN* for predicate nominative, or *PA* for predicate adjective. If a sentence does not have a complement, write *NONE.*

EXAMPLES ____PN____ 1. Lois is now an emergency room <u>nurse</u> in St. Paul.

____NONE____ 2. Mr. Baugh lives in Eau Claire, Wisconsin.

_____ 1. Jordan is anxious about the test results.

_____ 2. The Great Salt Lake is the largest inland body of salt water in the United States.

_____ 3. You must bathe the injured area with special care.

_____ 4. Give this warm bread to Ms. Bernstein.

_____ 5. Ernest Hemingway was famous for his simple prose.

_____ 6. Bananas are a good source of potassium.

_____ 7. That ice-skating maneuver looks tricky.

_____ 8. Thanh is leaving tomorrow for San Francisco.

_____ 9. Wayne eats a big salad for lunch twice a week.

_____ 10. The physician's assistant gave the girl a prescription.

| WORKSHEET 1 | **Identifying Simple and Compound Sentences (Rules 10 a, b)** |

EXERCISE A   On the line provided for each of the following sentences, write *S* if the sentence is a simple sentence and *C* if it is a compound sentence. Add a comma before the conjunction *and, but,* or *or* when necessary.

            EXAMPLE   _____C_____   **1.** Many people visit the Grand Canyon**,** but not everyone goes down into the canyon.

_____   **1.** We visited the Grand Canyon last summer.

_____   **2.** We were divided into small groups and each group was taken on a mule tour.

_____   **3.** I had been to the Grand Canyon before but this time I wanted to see every part of it.

_____   **4.** We saw sights twice as impressive as Niagara Falls.

_____   **5.** Some visitors stay on the north rim and observe the changing colors of the canyon.

_____   **6.** After the Grand Canyon, we went to the Navajo lands in northern New Mexico to see the beautiful scenery there.

_____   **7.** The famous Ship Rock in New Mexico was visible for miles.

_____   **8.** Finally, we went mountain biking in Moab, Utah.

_____   **9.** Did we spend the night in Blanding or did we stay in Monticello?

_____   **10.** I can't remember now; perhaps you do.

EXERCISE B   On the line provided for each of the following sentences, write a suitable conjunction to combine each pair of simple sentences into a compound sentence. Insert a comma in front of the conjunction *and, but, for, nor, or, so,* or *yet.*

            EXAMPLE   **1.** Jared will study to become a lawyer ___**,** *or*___ he will go to medical school.

1. The movie *Ben-Hur* is very long _____ I never lost interest in the story.

2. The director sent another helper an hour later _____ there was too much work for us to finish.

3. I have played several musical instruments _____ I like the trombone best.

4. You will have to hurry _____ you will be late for school.

5. Marissa and Janet did not want to wait in line for the roller coaster _____ they decided to ride the merry-go-round.

LANGUAGE HANDBOOK 10 KINDS OF SENTENCES

WORKSHEET 2 | Identifying Independent and Subordinate Clauses (Rule 10 c)

EXERCISE In the following sentences, underline each independent clause once and each subordinate clause twice. Not all the sentences have subordinate clauses.

EXAMPLE 1. The term *populist*, which means "of or for the common people," describes a movement in U.S. history.

1. The Populist movement was an American movement that developed in the late 1800s.

2. It began during the depression of the 1870s, when farmers were losing money.

3. The farmers organized cooperative groups, which were called Farmers' Alliances.

4. Members of these alliances hoped that farmers' expenses could be reduced by selling supplies at lower prices.

5. The alliances also built warehouses so that farmers could store their crops until prices were better.

6. Some alliances in the South included African American farmers.

7. Even though African Americans were not allowed to vote, the alliances included them.

8. By 1891, the movement was so strong that it became a national political party.

9. The alliances joined forces with an organization that was called the Knights of Labor.

10. The two groups formed the People's Party, whose members were known as Populists.

11. Populists wanted the national government to issue more paper money, which might raise farm prices.

12. The Populists wanted to form a national system that was similar to the local co-ops.

13. Populists also wanted a national income tax so that taxes could be collected more fairly.

14. So that working people could have more leisure time, the Populists wanted an eight-hour workday.

15. Populists pushed for the direct popular election of U.S. senators.

16. In 1892, the Populists had some success in the first national election in which they took part.

17. The Populists were strongest in 1896, when William Jennings Bryan won the party's presidential nomination.

18. Even though Bryan was a Democrat, he sympathized with the Populist cause.

19. When the Populists endorsed Bryan, they gave up their independent identity.

20. The brief Populist movement strongly influenced U.S. history, because almost all of its principles were later made into law.

| WORSHEET 3 | **Identifying Independent and Subordinate Clauses (Rule 10 d)** |

EXERCISE   In the following compound-complex sentences, underline each independent clause once and each subordinate clause twice.

EXAMPLES 1. <u>Louis went to the library yesterday</u>, and <u>while he was there</u> <u>he looked for a book</u> <u>that described the founding of his town</u>.

2. <u>Although Owen likes to entertain</u>, <u>he did not want to make a huge dinner</u>, nor <u>did he want to invite his guests to a restaurant</u>.

1. I could not remember where I put the serving dish, so I went back to the kitchen to get another one.

2. Portraits of many family ancestors hung in the corridor that ran the length of the house, yet they were not clearly visible because not enough light came through the window.

3. Two hours was a long time to wait, but Rennie willingly sat in the musty parlor while Samantha finished packing.

4. On our vacation, we went to the Bay of Fundy, which separates the Canadian provinces of New Brunswick and Nova Scotia, and we witnessed one of the highest tides in the world.

5. In Greek mythology, the Hydra was a nine-headed monster that lived in a marsh; when one of the heads was severed, two grew in its place.

6. Natalie wanted to have an autographed copy of Amy Tan's new book, so she purchased a copy and took it to the table in the bookstore where the author was sitting during a book-signing event.

7. Gabriela did not fully agree with the speaker, nor did she feel that he had focused enough on his topic.

8. When a television program is shot inside a studio, several cameras are often used; three or four cameras are focused on the same action at once, and the director chooses the best angle.

9. Chen wanted to take the Introduction to Computers course that was being taught on Monday and Wednesday mornings by Ms. Martelli, but his busy schedule prevented him from enrolling.

10. My family went to Costa Rica last summer, and my mother discovered that over a thousand species of orchids grow there.

LANGUAGE HANDBOOK 10 KINDS OF SENTENCES

WORKSHEET 4 | Identifying Independent and Subordinate Clauses (Rule 10 d)

EXERCISE   In the following compound-complex sentences, underline each independent clause once and each subordinate clause twice.

EXAMPLES 1. Dr. Daigle listened to what the patient had to say, but his face betrayed his skepticism.

2. When do you want to go the park, and what do you want to do after we leave there?

1. The student who scores highest on the exam will go to the finals, and the student with the second-highest score will receive special recognition at the annual awards banquet on May 25.

2. Don't believe everything that you read, for facts can be given a spin that makes them less reliable.

3. Yo-Yo Ma is an American cellist who is internationally known, and he has won ten Grammy Awards and several other awards for his recorded performances of both classical and popular music.

4. Before pottery was developed, food was eaten raw or roasted, but with pottery, people could cook in other ways.

5. Maribel explained that she had failed to take Tina's advice, for she had thought she knew better than Tina.

6. When my brother Tranh leaves for college at the Massachusetts Institute of Technology in Cambridge, I will move into his old bedroom, and I plan to paint it a more exciting color.

7. The South African runner Zola Budd attracted attention when she ran barefoot in competitions, yet running in her bare feet aggravated the injuries that she had already sustained.

8. The optician put drops in Rob's eyes, and when his pupils were dilated, she continued the exam.

9. You can wash the car and the sport utility vehicle now, but I would be happier if you would clean your room first.

10. Once Leah decided to run in the Over Hill and Dale Marathon, she began running six miles each weekday after school and band practice, and on weekends, she averaged ten miles a day.

LANGUAGE
HANDBOOK **10** KINDS OF SENTENCES

WORKSHEET 5 | **Classifying Sentences by Structure and by Purpose (Rules 10 a–h)**

EXERCISE A On the lines provided, classify the following sentences as *S* for simple, *CD* for compound, *CX* for complex, or *CD-CX* for compound-complex.

EXAMPLES   _*S*_   **1.** Please read me a story.

    _*CX*_   **2.** When you were a child, did you hear some of the Uncle Remus tales?

    _*CD*_   **3.** My mother read the tales to me, and my grandfather told me the stories from memory.

    _*CD-CX*_   **4.** When I am a parent, I'm sure I'll read the stories to my children, and they will love the tales, too.

_____ **1.** Joel Chandler Harris was born in 1848 in Eatonton, Georgia.

_____ **2.** He worked from 1862 to 1866 on a newspaper that was published by a Southern plantation owner, and during that time he became familiar with the stories and local African American legends.

_____ **3.** From 1866 to 1900, he worked on several newspapers in Georgia and Louisiana.

_____ **4.** He is most famous for his Uncle Remus stories, which have delighted generations of children.

_____ **5.** Harris began to publish these whimsical tales in the 1880s; they reproduced the oral folk tales of the local African American community.

_____ **6.** The tales center on the character of Uncle Remus, a former slave who is now the servant of a white Southern family.

_____ **7.** Uncle Remus entertains the children of this family when he relates stories about animals such as Brer Rabbit and Brer Bear.

_____ **8.** The Uncle Remus tales were among the first to use dialect to suggest a specific time and place, but the stories also address universal themes.

_____ **9.** The Uncle Remus stories are an important source of African American oral folk tales.

_____ **10.** Even though the tales were written more than one hundred years ago, they still fascinate readers.

Continued ☞

LANGUAGE HANDBOOK **10** **WORKSHEET 5** (continued)

EXERCISE B   On the lines provided, identify each of the following sentences as *DEC* for declarative, *IMP* for imperative, *INT* for interrogative, or *EXC* for exclamatory. Then, add the necessary end mark.

EXAMPLES   __*DEC*__   **1.** My brother Rick and I are planning a surprise party for our cousin Adam**.**

__*EXC*__   **2.** It will be such fun**!**

_____   **1.** Will you help us

_____   **2.** Listen to our plans so far

_____   **3.** We've invited fifteen of his friends

_____   **4.** Everyone is bringing party supplies

_____   **5.** They're supposed to arrive at least thirty minutes before Adam is expected

_____   **6.** His mother is involved in the planning, of course

_____   **7.** How do you think she's going to get him out of the house

_____   **8.** She's going to take him shopping for a present

_____   **9.** What a clever idea

_____   **10.** While they are gone, we will decorate the house

_____   **11.** Do you know where we can get a "Happy Birthday" banner made

_____   **12.** I saw a colorful one once at someone else's birthday party

_____   **13.** We need some candles that he can't blow out

_____   **14.** David, can we ask your father to get helium for the balloons

_____   **15.** Luis, please bring lots of crepe paper streamers

_____   **16.** I think we should plan to have games

_____   **17.** Do you think we should have lemonade or juice

_____   **18.** My brother Rick is in charge of refreshments

_____   **19.** I am supposed to buy a present from Rick and me, but I don't know what Adam wants

_____   **20.** Do you have any ideas

_____   **21.** What a surprise Adam will have when he gets back

_____   **22.** Even though we've been careful, I wonder if he suspects anything

_____   **23.** Don't say a word to anyone about the plans

_____   **24.** If you can't come, please let me know as soon as possible

_____   **25.** I can hardly wait

LANGUAGE HANDBOOK 10 KINDS OF SENTENCES

WORKSHEET 6 | Test (Rules 10 a–h)

EXERCISE A   On the line provided, classify each of the following sentences as *S* for simple, *CD* for compound, *CX* for complex, or *CD-CX* for compound-complex.

EXAMPLE ____*CX*____ **1.** When you were seven, what was the most important thing in your life?

_____ **1.** Eleazar has relatives who live in Quito, Ecuador, and he intends to visit them after the spring semester is over.

_____ **2.** Do you understand what the teacher wants us to do, or are you as confused as I am?

_____ **3.** The leader of the wolf pack struck off on its own through the snow.

_____ **4.** Jenny has eaten vegetables enthusiastically since she was a baby, but she especially likes carrots and spinach.

_____ **5.** Are you going to the carnival tomorrow night, or do you have to work?

_____ **6.** I admire Thomas Jefferson because when he attempted to create a new government, he constantly had the freedom and well-being of the individual in mind.

_____ **7.** Would you enjoy living in a place where it never snows?

_____ **8.** The generosity of Ms. Petrakis, my neighbor, never ceases to amaze me.

_____ **9.** The mule refused to move another inch, for she was exhausted from the day's work.

_____ **10.** Can you imagine what the world would be like if electricity had not been harnessed?

EXERCISE B   On the line provided, identify each of the following sentences as *DEC* for declarative, *IMP* for imperative, *INT* for interrogative, or *EXC* for exclamatory. Then, add the necessary end mark.

EXAMPLE ____*DEC*____ **1.** My family is traveling to Detroit.

_____ **1.** Would you like to go with us

_____ **2.** I had no idea there were so many things to do in Detroit until I started reading about it

_____ **3.** Read this article published by the Detroit Chamber of Commerce

_____ **4.** Do you think that my family will enjoy the trip

_____ **5.** My father can go to a Red Wings hockey game at the Joe Louis Arena

Continued ☞

_____ **6.** How happy my brother will be as he tours Tiger Stadium

_____ **7.** My mom will get to see the Diego Rivera mural at the Detroit Institute of the Arts

_____ **8.** My sister, who is interested in history, can spend time at Greenfield Village, a collection of historical houses and workshops

_____ **9.** Would you like to spend time in the movie theaters and shops of the Renaissance Center

_____ **10.** I can't wait until we get there

EXERCISE C On the lines provided, classify the following sentences as *S* for simple, *CD* for compound, *CX* for complex, or *CD-CX* for compound-complex. Then, identify the italicized clause by writing *IND* for independent or *SUB* for subordinate.

EXAMPLE __CD-CX; IND__ **1.** *The most recent recording* that Stevie Wonder produced *was good,* but I like his earlier music better.

_____ **1.** *Stevie Wonder is a well-known singer and songwriter* who has won several Grammy Awards.

_____ **2.** *He was born in 1950 in Saginaw, Michigan;* his name at birth was Steveland Morris.

_____ **3.** *Although he had been blind since infancy,* Wonder began to play the piano at four years old and was a proficient singer and instrumentalist by the age of thirteen.

_____ **4.** He was thirteen *when his first hit was released by Motown Records,* and at that time he was given his professional name.

_____ **5.** *He has composed much of his work with the help of Syreeta Wright,* who was his wife.

_____ **6.** *Wonder experimented with synthesizers,* and he was one of the first musicians to include electronic music in African American popular music.

_____ **7.** *In 1973, the musician survived a car accident,* which nearly killed him.

_____ **8.** Wonder, *who had already won several Grammy Awards,* won three more of them in 1996.

_____ **9.** *Wonder has also been an activist for social causes,* two of which are the anti-apartheid movement in South Africa and Mothers Against Drunk Driving.

_____ **10.** Wonder has recorded several hits, *which include "Superstition" and "You Are the Sunshine of My Life."*

Continued ☞

Elements of Literature

LANGUAGE HANDBOOK 10 **WORKSHEET 6** *(continued)*

EXERCISE D   On the lines provided, write a sentence that has the structure indicated and includes the independent or subordinate clause that is provided. Note that *CD* indicates *compound*, *CX* indicates *complex*, and *CD-CX* indicates *compound-complex*.

> **EXAMPLE** 1. (CX) *as soon as he gets home*   <u>Usually, Leon does his</u>
> <u>homework as soon as he gets home.</u>

1. (CX) *that is hard to believe* _____

_____

2. (CX) *The books are on the top shelf* _____

_____

3. (CD) *Rosetta will not go near the water* _____

_____

4. (CX) *unless the train arrives on time* _____

_____

5. (CD-CX) *even though the dog is three months old* _____

_____

_____

6. (CD-CX) *since Evan's grandfather had planted it* _____

_____

_____

7. (CD) *The Morrisons traveled throughout Central America* ____

_____

_____

8. (CD) *The song reminded Mary of something in her past* _____

_____

_____

9. (CX) *so that Charlene can finish the project* _____

_____

_____

10. (CD-CX) *The moccasins were in an old chest* _____

_____

_____

LANGUAGE HANDBOOK 11 WRITING EFFECTIVE SENTENCES

WORKSHEET 1 Correcting Run-on Sentences (Rule 11 a)

EXERCISE Correct each of the following run-on sentences by capitalizing and punctuating it as two separate sentences. Cross out each incorrect comma or lowercase letter, and write the correct period or capital letter above it. If an item is already a complete sentence, write *C* on the line provided.

EXAMPLES _____ 1. Each year thousands of Americans visit Canada. Some have summer homes near Canada's beautiful lakes and rivers.

_____C_____ 2. Because it is such a vast country, Canada offers a wide range of tourist attractions.

_____ 1. The St. Lawrence Seaway opened the Great Lakes to large ocean vessels, a cruise up the seaway makes a pleasant vacation.

_____ 2. Travelers may also take boat trips from Seattle to Victoria, British Columbia, then they can go on to Vancouver from Victoria.

_____ 3. By shopping in Victoria and Vancouver, tourists can find their favorite British products.

_____ 4. Fine bone china cups and saucers are available, collecting these is a hobby for many people.

_____ 5. A popular resort area is the town of Banff, Alberta, and Lake Louise, a region of great beauty.

_____ 6. A trip through the Canadian Rockies is memorable, many of the rugged mountains are covered with snow all summer.

_____ 7. Churchill, near Hudson Bay, is the gateway to the far North and the base of many arctic expeditions.

_____ 8. The Calgary Stampede is a popular attraction, it features bareback riding and other events.

_____ 9. The Canadian side of Niagara Falls is beautiful, you can go right up to the Horseshoe Falls.

_____ 10. A trip to Ottawa, Ontario, should include a visit to the stately buildings of Canada's Parliament, they are built in the Gothic style.

LANGUAGE HANDBOOK 11 — WRITING EFFECTIVE SENTENCES

WORKSHEET 2 — Correcting and Revising Run-on Sentences (Rule 11 a)

EXERCISE A Correct the run-on sentences in the following paragraphs by inserting periods and capital letters where needed. Cross out each incorrect comma or lowercase letter, and write the correct period or capital letter above it. Be careful not to create any sentence fragments.

EXAMPLE Our local TV weatherman is very knowledgeable. He has a degree in meteorology.

Today, when modern meteorologists forecast the weather, they can count on the help of an impressive battery of scientific devices. Weather satellites, for example, relay photographs of cloud formations from all over the world these pictures show where storms are beginning over oceans and deserts the paths of typhoons and hurricanes are tracked in the same way. Weather information from all sources is fed into powerful computers, thus the weather can be evaluated with amazing speed.

Our ancestors had no complicated weather instruments they had to rely on their eyes and ears and a few old proverbs and maxims. Their methods were hardly scientific, however, some were founded on fact. Today, for example, no one still believes the old superstition about the groundhog, but we celebrate Groundhog Day just the same. If the groundhog sees its shadow on the second day of February, there will be six more weeks of winter, watch for yourself and see! The behavior of insects, on the other hand, is still a good indicator of temperature because insects are coldblooded. Grasshoppers cannot fly when the temperature drops below 55 degrees Fahrenheit if you hear a cricket chirping, count the number of chirps in fourteen seconds and add forty, then you will have the temperature in degrees Fahrenheit.

Today, weather forecasting is more accurate, if less picturesque, than it was in the old days, however, the forecasters are not always right, perhaps because there are so many factors to consider.

Continued ☞

EXERCISE B   On the lines provided, revise each group of words that is a run-on sentence. Run-on sentences may be revised by making them into separate sentences or by joining them with a comma and *and, but,* or *or.* If the group of words is already correct, write *C.*

EXAMPLE **1.** My uncle teaches at the University of Miami it is in Coral Gables, Florida. *My uncle teaches at the University of Miami.*
It is in Coral Gables, Florida.

1. He invited me to visit him we went many places around Miami. _____
_____

2. We could go to the animal park we could go to the aquarium we did not have time to go to both. _____
_____

3. We went to the animal park I saw a Komodo dragon. _____
_____

4. We also saw tree kangaroos they are very cute. _____
_____

5. The animals all have large areas to live in and are not in cages. _____
_____

6. The animals are not in cages they cannot get out. _____
_____

7. The elephants live in big areas they are able to live normal lives. _____
_____

8. Different exhibits deal with the continents of Asia, Africa, and Europe the Asian exhibit includes rare white Bengal tigers. _____
_____
_____

9. The African plains exhibit has giraffes, zebras, and ostriches living together as they do in the wild a gorilla family also lives among them. _____
_____
_____

10. The animal park is the best one I ever visited I hope to go back again soon. _____
_____

LANGUAGE HANDBOOK **11** WRITING EFFECTIVE SENTENCES

WORKSHEET 3 | **Combining Choppy Sentences by Inserting Words (Rule 11 b)**

EXERCISE On the lines provided, combine each of the following groups of sentences into one complete sentence by inserting words from one sentence into the other sentence. Be sure to add commas where necessary.

EXAMPLE 1. Mount Everest is a famous mountain.
It is the most famous mountain in the world. *Mount Everest is the most famous mountain in the world.*

1. The Himalayas are mountains in Asia.

   They are the tallest mountains in Asia. _____

   _____

   _____

2. You can see a view of Mount Everest from Darjeeling.

   It is a beautiful view. _____

   _____

   _____

3. Tea bushes grow on the slopes of the hills near Darjeeling.

   The slopes are steep.

   The hills are fertile. _____

   _____

   _____

4. The Sherpas are people who live in Nepal.

   They are Tibetan people.

   They live in northeast Nepal. _____

   _____

   _____

5. Tenzing Norgay was a Sherpa.

   Tenzing Norgay was a guide.

   Tenzing Norgay was one of the first mountain climbers to reach the top of Mount Everest. _____

   _____

   _____

Continued ☞

6. The danger in mountain climbing comes from the altitude and the cold.

The greatest danger comes from these things.

The altitude is high.

The cold is bitter. _____

_____

_____

7. The sun reflecting on the snow can cause blindness.

The sun is bright.

The snow is white.

The blindness is temporary. _____

_____

_____

8. The air at that altitude makes oxygen masks necessary.

The air is thin.

The altitude is high.

The oxygen masks are expensive. _____

_____

_____

9. The cold can cause frostbite on fingers and toes.

The cold is penetrating.

The frostbite can be severe.

The fingers and toes are exposed. _____

_____

_____

10. Climbers need boots and food for reaching altitudes.

The boots must be light.

They must also be durable.

The food should be nutritious.

The altitudes are high. _____

_____

_____

WORKSHEET 4 | **Combining Choppy Sentences by Inserting Phrases (Rule 11 b)**

EXERCISE A On the lines provided, combine each group of sentences into one sentence by inserting prepositional phrases from one sentence into another.

EXAMPLE **1.** Alexander the Great was born in 356 B.C.
He was born in the city of Pella.
He was born in Macedonia. _Alexander the Great was born_
in 356 B.C. in the city of Pella in Macedonia.

1. Alexander the Great's father was the king.

He was the king of Macedonia. _____

_____

2. When Alexander was young, he saw some wild horses.

The horses were in the marketplace. _____

_____

3. One horse threw anyone who dared to ride it.

It was a horse with a deep black coat. _____

_____

4. Alexander's father, Philip, wanted to destroy the black horse.

It was the horse with the mean temper. _____

_____

5. Alexander noticed the shadow.

The shadow was in front of the horse. _____

_____

6. The horse's shadow moved as the horse jumped.

The shadow moved on the ground. _____

_____

7. Alexander recognized the horse's fear.

It was the fear of its own shadow. _____

_____

8. He grabbed the reins and turned the animal around.

The reins were on the horse. _____

Continued ☞

9. The horse no longer saw its frightening shadow.

   The horse did not see its shadow in this direction.

   The shadow was on the ground. _____

   _____

10. The story is an example.

    The story is about Alexander the Great taming the black horse.

    It is an example of his intelligence and compassion. _____

    _____

    _____

EXERCISE B   On the lines provided, combine each group of sentences into one sentence by using participial phrases.

> EXAMPLE 1. My aunt Nora makes her living as a computer consultant.
>   She flies from city to city. _Flying from city to city, my aunt_
>   _Nora makes her living as a computer consultant._

1. She is employed by a large consulting firm.

   Nora is one of the firm's most successful consultants. _____

   _____

2. She is able to answer her clients' questions at all times.

   She carries a mobile phone with her. _____

   _____

3. She is known nationwide for her skill in solving computer problems.

   She is often the first person requested by a company in need. _____

   _____

   _____

4. Nora is sometimes a company's last hope to save their computer files.

   She rides to the rescue. _____

   _____

   _____

5. She is regarded as one of the best by other members of her profession.

   Last year she won an award from a national association of computer consultants.

   _____

   _____

| WORKSHEET 5 | ## Combining Choppy Sentences by Using *And, But,* or *Or* (Rule 11 b) |

EXERCISE A   On the lines provided, combine each group of sentences into one sentence that has a compound subject, a compound verb, or both a compound subject and a compound verb. Be sure each verb agrees in number with its subject.

> EXAMPLE **1.** Marcy wants to go camping during summer vacation. Her friend Naomi wants to go camping during summer vacation. *Marcy and her friend Naomi want to go camping during summer vacation.*

1. They will hike in Rocky Mountain National Park.

They will pitch their tents in Hidden Valley. _____

_____

_____

2. Last year Marcy walked up Trail Ridge to the alpine meadows.

She went fishing in the Fall River. _____

_____

_____

3. Naomi is interested in watching for bighorn sheep.

Marcy is interested in watching for bighorn sheep. _____

_____

_____

4. Sheep usually graze on the high slopes.

Sheep wander down near Sheep Lake. _____

_____

_____

5. Marcy has plenty of equipment for camping.

Naomi has plenty of equipment for camping. _____

_____

_____

6. The pair will eat freeze-dried food.

They will enjoy fish caught in the brooks and lakes. _____

_____

_____

Continued ☞

7. Marcy may clean the fish and cook them.

Naomi may clean the fish and cook them. _____

_____

8. Naomi's father will drive out for the weekend.

He will take them hiking above the timberline. _____

_____

_____

9. Camping is among the girls' favorite pastimes.

Hiking is among the girls' favorite pastimes. _____

_____

10. Marcy is looking forward to the trip.

Naomi is looking forward to the trip.

Both are excited about camping in the mountains. _____

_____

_____

EXERCISE B   Most of the following groups of sentences consist of two or more closely related sentences. On the lines provided, combine these sentences into a single compound sentence using the conjunctions *and, but,* or *or.* If a group of sentences consists of unrelated sentences, do not combine these sentences, but write *U* for unrelated.

   EXAMPLE 1. Benjamin Franklin was an author and a statesman.
              Many people remember him best as an inventor. *Benjamin*
              Franklin was an author and a statesman, but many people
              remember him best as an inventor.

1. Benjamin Franklin was an apprentice printer for his brother James.

He did not like working for him. _____

_____

_____

2. Franklin read many books after work.

In his writing he tried to copy the authors' styles. _____

_____

_____

Continued ☞

3. Franklin and his brother printed the newspaper.

   Franklin also had to sell the paper on the street. _____

   _____

   _____

4. The paper sold well.

   The paper attacked the Massachusetts Assembly. _____

   _____

   _____

5. Franklin could stay in Boston to work for his brother.

   He could run away to seek his fortune. _____

   _____

   _____

6. He first went to New York City.

   There was no work for printers in that city. _____

   _____

   _____

7. He took a ferry to Perth Amboy, New Jersey.

   A storm drove the ferry onto the rocks. _____

   _____

   _____

8. He walked most of the way to Philadelphia.

   This city was bigger than New York or Boston. _____

   _____

   _____

9. Franklin finally started his own print shop.

   It became successful very quickly. _____

   _____

   _____

10. Benjamin Franklin started *Poor Richard's Almanac.*

    This publication made him famous. _____

    _____

    _____

LANGUAGE HANDBOOK 11 · WRITING EFFECTIVE SENTENCES

WORKSHEET 6 | **Combining Choppy Sentences by Using Subordinate Clauses (Rule 11 b)**

EXERCISE A   On the lines provided, combine each pair of sentences into one complete sentence by making the italicized sentence an adjective clause. Be sure the clause comes right after the word it modifies.

EXAMPLE 1. Yellowstone National Park is famous for its geysers and bubbling hot springs. *It is bigger than the state of Delaware.* Yellowstone National Park, which is bigger than the state of Delaware, is famous for its geysers and bubbling hot springs.

1. A newer park is called Gates of the Arctic National Park.

   It is four times the size of Yellowstone National Park. _____

   _____

2. Many national parks are crowded with visitors.

   These visitors may threaten the natural environment. _____

   _____

3. One national park in Hawaii contains active volcanoes.

   They sometimes spew fire and lava. _____

   _____

4. Forest rangers work deep within the national forest.

   Most people never see the rangers. _____

   _____

5. At Mesa Verde National Park you can climb down into kivas.

   They were built by ancient cliff dwellers. _____

   _____

6. My aunt Laura's job is guiding rafts down the Colorado River.

   Her job is filled with danger. _____

   _____

7. In Virginia there is a national monument to Booker T. Washington.

   He made many contributions to education. _____ _____

   _____

   _____

Continued ☞

8. Dinosaur National Monument is in Colorado.

This monument interests me the most of all monuments. _____

_____

9. Terry will enjoy Acadia National Park.

Terry loves to camp by the sea. _____

_____

10. Rangers scan the horizon for forest fires.

They live in tall watchtowers. _____

_____

EXERCISE B   On the lines provided, combine each pair of sentences into one complete sentence by changing the second sentence to an adverb clause. Use the subordinating conjunction in parentheses to introduce the adverb clause. Add commas where necessary.

EXAMPLE **1.** Our teacher saw us studying hard.
She came into the classroom. (*when*) *Our teacher saw us studying hard when she came into the classroom.*

1. Many people want to be ballet dancers.

Ballet dancing seems to be a glamorous profession. (*because*) _____

_____

_____

2. The United States Constitution will last another two hundred years.

We maintain our love for freedom. (*if*) _____

_____

_____

3. We sat through movie matinees every Saturday.

We were seven or eight years old. (*when*) _____

_____

_____

Continued ☞

4. Melinda is not eligible to run again.

She won the election last year. (*since*) _____

_____

_____

5. Preston wants to exercise every day.

He can stay fit. (*so that*) _____

_____

_____

6. There is trouble.

There are hungry bears and unguarded campsites. (*wherever*) _____

_____

_____

7. We will do all our shopping in this store.

The choice of merchandise is limited. (*although*) _____

_____

_____

_____

8. An athlete has no chance to enter the Olympics.

He or she begins training very early. (*unless*) _____

_____

_____

_____

9. The pitcher threw warm-up tosses.

The batter took some practice swings. (*while*) _____

_____

_____

_____

10. Marsha had already received her prize in the mail.

Phil collected all thirty-three box tops. (*before*) _____

_____

_____

_____

| WORKSHEET 7 | **Revising Stringy and Wordy Sentences (Rule 11 c)** |

EXERCISE A   On the lines provided, revise the following stringy sentences by breaking each of them into two or more sentences, or by turning some of the independent clauses into phrases or subordinate clauses.

EXAMPLE **1.** Argentina is a country in South America and it borders the south Atlantic and its capital is Buenos Aires. _Argentina is a country in South America that borders the south Atlantic. Its capital is Buenos Aires._

1. Tanmoor is an interesting character, and he is in a story Jessica wrote, and he is from a small town in Argentina, but he wants to go to a big city. _____

_____

_____

2. The story is about Tanmoor, and it has an exciting beginning, and it opens with his father working on a ranch. _____

_____

_____

3. Some rustlers come to the ranch, a group of bankers arrives, and angry neighbors visit, and tension mounts. _____

_____

_____

4. Tanmoor's father is a *vaquero*, and a *vaquero* is a cowboy, and a *vaquero* has a lot of responsibility. _____

_____

_____

5. Tanmoor's father is named Carlos, but his nickname is Coco, and he is trusted by the ranch owners. _____

_____

_____

Continued ☞

6. Tanmoor helps his father, and he enjoys the work, but Tanmoor wants to own his own business, and he wants this business to be in the city. _____

_____

_____

_____

7. He is a smart boy, and he likes to figure out people, so he watches their expressions, and he watches their movements. _____

_____

_____

_____

8. Tanmoor identifies the rustlers, and he tricks the bankers, and he calms the neighbors, and he restores peace to the ranch. _____

_____

_____

_____

9. Jessica modeled the character Tanmoor after her brother, and her brother's name is Tom Andrew, and the family's last name is Moore. _____

_____

_____

_____

10. Tom Moore reads a lot, and he reads many books about South America, and he can tell you all about its major cities. _____

_____

_____

_____

EXERCISE B   On the lines provided, revise the following wordy sentences by replacing a group of words with one word, by replacing a clause with a phrase, or by taking out a group of unnecessary words.

> EXAMPLE **1.** When the daughters of pioneers were young girls, they learned how to sew and cook. *Young daughters of pioneers learned how to sew and cook.*

1. I usually order a large salad when we go out to eat at a restaurant. _____

Continued ☞

2. After the game was over and finished, my voice was hoarse from yelling. _____
_____
_____

3. With a quick movement of her hands, Nana turned the hot tortillas with her fingers.
_____
_____
_____

4. Mariah knows all of the state capitals that are the centers of government in each state.
_____
_____
_____

5. We passed the pavilion as a woman yelled in a loud voice. _____
_____
_____

6. Have you memorized the "I Have a Dream" speech by Martin Luther King, Jr., so that
you can recite it by heart? ___ _____
_____
_____

7. Much to the astonishment of everyone who was present, the window did not break.
_____
_____
_____

8. The scientist examined the insect and studied it closely. _____
_____
_____

9. Before the class resumes again, we can go over our homework. _____
_____
_____

10. The sound of the thunder was so loud it was alarming. _____
_____
_____

LANGUAGE HANDBOOK **11** WRITING EFFECTIVE SENTENCES

| WORKSHEET 8 | Test (Rules 11 a–c) |

EXERCISE A   On the lines provided, revise each of the following run-on sentences by making two sentences or by joining them with a comma and a conjunction.

> EXAMPLE **1.** The word *cryonics* refers to the practice of freezing human bodies it comes from the Greek word for "cold."
> *The word cryonics refers to the practice of freezing human*
> *bodies. It comes from the Greek word for "cold."*

1. Believers in the movement are frozen upon death their bodies are kept in special temperature-controlled units. _____

_____

_____

2. Scientists may eventually find cures for all terminal diseases patients in cryonic suspension will then be brought back to life. _____

_____

_____

3. Science fiction writers often include suspended animation in their stories and films they use it to explain how astronauts could make journeys lasting hundreds of years.

_____

_____

4. In the movie *Planet of the Apes,* astronauts put themselves into suspended animation for a long space voyage when they wake up, they find themselves on a planet inhabited by intelligent apes. _____

_____

_____

5. Several sequels to this movie have been produced one sequel features the apes releasing an alien virus. _____

_____

_____

Continued ☞

EXERCISE B   On the lines provided, rewrite each of the following paragraphs by combining sentences in the four ways you have learned in this chapter. You will need to leave out repetitious words and do some rearranging in order to make the paragraph read more smoothly. Make all the changes you think are needed, but do not change the meaning of the paragraph. Add correct punctuation.

EXAMPLE   Hurricane Mitch was a hurricane. It was a dangerous hurricane. It caused billions of dollars of damage in Central America.
Hurricane Mitch was a dangerous hurricane that caused billions of dollars of damage in Central America.

Hurricanes are tropical storms. The storms are powerful. Hurricanes form over water. It is ocean water. The water is warm. The water is near the equator. A hurricane produces energy. A hurricane can produce as much energy as several thousand atomic bombs. A hurricane produces this much energy in a second. The energy is spread over an area. The area is several hundred miles. Winds in a hurricane blow more than 75 miles per hour. These winds sometimes reach 120 miles per hour. Hurricanes move over land. They cause great devastation. The devastation is caused by their winds. Now meteorologists track hurricanes. They track them accurately. The meteorologists can predict their paths. People can be evacuated before a hurricane arrives. _____

_____

_____

_____

_____

_____

_____

_____

_____

_____

_____

_____

_____

_____

Continued ☞

Emily Dickinson lived during the nineteenth century. She has become an interesting subject for biographers. She wrote a great deal of poetry. She wrote chiefly for herself. She sometimes wrote for a few friends. She wrote many of her poems on scraps of paper. They were beautiful poems. She hid the scraps of paper in a drawer. She studied at Mount Holyoke Female Seminary. It is in Massachusetts. She studied there for a short while. Then she became a recluse. She seldom left her house. She wore white dresses. She wore them always. No one knows exactly why.

_____

_____

_____

_____

_____

_____

_____

_____

_____

_____

_____

EXERCISE C   On the lines provided, revise the following stringy sentences by breaking each of them into two or more sentences, or by turning some of the independent clauses into phrases or subordinate clauses.

EXAMPLE 1. People who have pets need to keep them in safe places, and they need to watch out for them, and not let them run loose, and not let them go out into the street. *People who have pets need to watch out for them and keep them in safe places. Pets should be kept from running loose and getting into the street.*

1. The puppy ran into the street, and it was raining, and the car skidded, and it missed the puppy. _____

_____

Continued ☞

2. The assignment was long, and I was tired, but it was easy, so I finished before supper.

_____

_____

_____

3. The movie started on time, but we were late, so we missed the first ten minutes, and I was upset. _____

_____

_____

4. Rosh Hashana is tomorrow, and it is the Jewish New Year, and I am allowed to miss school for it. _____

_____

_____

5. Oxford shoes are popular now, so my brother has a pair, and they are black, and I like them. _____

_____

_____

EXERCISE D   On the lines provided, revise each of the following wordy sentences by replacing a group of words with one word, by replacing a clause with a phrase, or by taking out a group of unnecessary words.

> EXAMPLE **1.** In recent days I have been climbing up the stairs for exercise. *Recently I have been climbing stairs for exercise.*

1. With a great deal of pride, I accepted the award. _____

_____

2. After the dance was over, we went for a walk along the beach. _____

_____

3. Whenever you like, you will always be welcome in my home. _____

_____

4. Make sure you sharpen all your pencils and that they are sharpened before you take the test. _____

_____

5. The mamba is a kind of tree snake that comes from the continent of Africa. _____

_____

LANGUAGE HANDBOOK **12** CAPITAL LETTERS

| WORKSHEET 1 | **Using Capital Letters Correctly (Rules 12 a–d)**

EXERCISE A   Circle the letters that should be capitalized in the following sentences.

EXAMPLE **1.** ⓣhe letter ⓘ mailed to my grandmother in Arizona arrived the next day.

1. did Ms. Lamas say, "fill the piñatas for Cinco de Mayo"?
2. My sister is so dramatic; every morning she says, "greetings, o dawn of a new day!"
3. Joyce Kilmer wrote a poem that begins, "I think that i shall never see / A poem lovely as a tree."
4. the results of the spelling bee prove that i can think under pressure.
5. The minister ended her prayer by saying, "hear us, o Lord, today and always."
6. The most recent story we read for class was "The Treasure of Lemon Brown" by walter dean myers.
7. After reading the story, we discussed Lemon Brown's statement, "every man got a treasure."
8. Should Jamie and i go to the library now or later?
9. our town's sister city is saumur, france.
10. The voice over the loudspeaker said, "flash floods are expected. school will be dismissed at noon."

EXERCISE B   In the following paragraph, circle the ten letters that should be capitalized.

EXAMPLE   We drove through Iowa ⓒity, ⓘowa, on our way to Sioux ⓕalls, ⓢouth ⓓakota.

Last summer my family and i went to Mandan, north dakota, to see the dedication of a monument to American Indian cultures. We attended a nighttime ceremony, where a speaker began by saying, "we are one with you and each other, o Great Spirit." As we sat on the ground under the constellation orion and thousands of other stars, I felt a strong connection with the universe. The next day we visited Fort Abraham Lincoln State park where the Heart river and the missouri river meet.

LANGUAGE HANDBOOK **12** CAPITAL LETTERS

| WORSHEET 2 | **Capitalizing Proper Nouns (Rule 12 d)** |

EXERCISE   On the line provided, write the letter *A* or *B* to indicate which column contains the correctly capitalized phrase for each item.

	A	**B**
EXAMPLE ___*B*___ **1.**	the big dipper	the Big Dipper

	A	**B**
1.	the Red cross	the Red Cross
2.	the Baker Medical Building	the baker Medical Building
3.	Freemont junior high school	Freemont Junior High School
4.	world war I	World War I
5.	a modern building	a modern Building
6.	the Roman Empire	the Roman empire
7.	The Rivera Supply company	the Rivera Supply Company
8.	Memorial day	Memorial Day
9.	Trinity Church	Trinity church
10.	Arcadia Motor Company	Arcadia Motor company
11.	our new School	our new school
12.	Wing's Bakery Shop	Wing's Bakery shop
13.	the supreme court	the Supreme Court
14.	United States congress	United States Congress
15.	Stanford University	Stanford university
16.	the fourth of July	the Fourth of July
17.	the Bureau of mines	the Bureau of Mines
18.	last summer	last Summer
19.	the U.S. National Tennis Tournament	the U.S. national tennis tournament
20.	April fools' day	April Fools' Day
21.	Vietnam war	Vietnam War
22.	the Everglades National Park	the Everglades national park
23.	olympic games	Olympic Games
24.	the Mississippi River	the Mississippi river
25.	Salt Lake city, Utah	Salt Lake City, Utah

LANGUAGE HANDBOOK **12** CAPITAL LETTERS

| WORSHEET 3 | Capitalizing Proper Nouns (Rule 12 d)

EXERCISE A Add capital letters where necessary in the following sentences by drawing a line through each incorrect lowercase letter and writing the correct capital letter above it. If a sentence is already correct, write *C* on the line provided.

EXAMPLE _____ **1.** My friend ̶betty ̶underwood has traveled all
over the ̶united ̶states.

_____ **1.** Although she now lives in the east, she liked living in california best.

_____ **2.** Her family lived in chicago, new york, st. louis, and san francisco.

_____ **3.** The underwoods have tried to learn about each area where they have lived.

_____ **4.** Because they like the water, they always try to find a house near a lake, river, or shoreline.

_____ **5.** Now they live in a suburb north of boston called wayland and swim in lake cochichuate.

_____ **6.** When the underwoods lived in san francisco, their house was only a block from san francisco bay.

_____ **7.** Betty loved to cross the golden gate bridge and ride the cable cars on california street.

_____ **8.** Her sister, alicia, attended classes at the university of california at berkeley.

_____ **9.** There she studied world religions like buddhism and islam.

_____ **10.** Followers of islam are called muslims.

_____ **11.** When the family moved to st. louis, they had trouble finding a home near the water.

_____ **12.** The mississippi river is too muddy to swim in, and its current is very swift.

_____ **13.** In chicago, the family lived in wilmette at 187 tenth avenue.

_____ **14.** They often saw the chicago cubs play at wrigley field.

_____ **15.** The baseball field is at 1060 west addison boulevard.

_____ **16.** After she graduates from high school, Betty would like to attend the university of chicago, which is in hyde park.

_____ **17.** She wants to study the art of ancient greece.

_____ **18.** After Betty finishes college, she wants to travel.

_____ **19.** She wants to live in paris and study at the university of paris.

_____ **20.** Betty would visit the louvre and study the paintings of monet and cassatt.

Continued ☞

EXERCISE B   Circle the letters that should be capitalized in the following sentences.

EXAMPLE 1. Duke (u)niversity is in (d)urham, (n)orth (c)arolina.

1. Have you ever been to southern california?

2. Isn't gary, indiana, near chicago?

3. Daniel was awarded a purple heart for bravery in the vietnam war.

4. My mother recently read a biography of the anthropologist margaret mead.

5. Hudson bay is very far north, beyond lake superior.

6. My mother met my father on the ferry to cape charles, virginia.

7. The north wind is quite cold in calgary, alberta.

8. Most of the religions in the world are based on belief in god, the supreme being.

9. Let's go swimming in chippewa lake.

10. Charles lindbergh was the first person to fly solo across the atlantic ocean.

11. I will start my job with the c. o. miller company next monday.

12. We are studying the art of the italian renaissance.

13. Classes at wade junior high school start on the thursday after labor day.

14. The National science fair takes place right after spring vacation.

15. I enjoyed the michigan state fair, which opened last saturday.

16. Veterans day was originally called armistice day, in commemoration of the end of world war I on november 11, 1918.

17. We visited the united states senate, the house of representatives, and the treasury building during our student tour of washington, D.C.

18. They attended martin luther king, jr., high school in akron, ohio.

19. The moon lamp Company has a mailing address at grand central station.

20. During the fall and winter there are several holidays, such as thanksgiving, christmas, and New year's day.

21. Patrick and colleen murphy make a wonderful irish stew of mutton and vegetables.

22. Our neighbor james dowden plans to take a long vacation to australia, new zealand, and hong kong.

23. In 1998 and 1999, NASA launched six separate spacecraft in six months, including *deep space 1* and *mars polar lander*.

24. This summer my family and the johnson family are driving to the petrified forest national park in arizona.

25. Mount whitney is the highest peak in the sierra nevada in eastern california.

LANGUAGE HANDBOOK 12 CAPITAL LETTERS

| WORSHEET 4 | **Capitalizing Proper Adjectives and School Subjects (Rules 12 e, f)** |

EXERCISE A   Circle the letters that should be capitalized in the following sentences.

> **EXAMPLE 1.** Some people think jazz is the only original (a)merican music.

1. Most jazz rhythms come from african music.

2. Great jazz can be heard in many louisiana cities.

3. The original jazz bands were the bourbon street groups, which marched in funerals in New Orleans.

4. Two famous african american jazz performers were Billie Holiday and Duke Ellington.

5. West indian music, such as the caribbean calypso, is a mixture of african and spanish influences.

6. The jamaican steel bands produce a unique sound.

7. Some jamaican musicians play fantastic music on instruments made from old oil drums and other scrap materials.

8. In Puerto Rico, one needs to know the spanish language to enjoy oneself fully.

9. Puerto Ricans have always been very proud of their latin american heritage.

10. Most tourists come back from Puerto Rico eager to learn caribbean dances.

EXERCISE B   Add capital letters where necessary in the following sentences by drawing a line through each incorrect lowercase letter and writing the correct capital letter above it. If a sentence is already correct, write *C* on the line provided.

> **EXAMPLE** _____ **1.** My grandmother purchased a ~~c~~hinese painting.   *C*

_____ 1. That row of houses is an excellent example of georgian architecture.

_____ 2. Will astronomy be covered in science I?

_____ 3. My father collects danish glassware.

_____ 4. We had some french toast for breakfast.

_____ 5. The radio announcer spoke with an english accent.

_____ 6. You can still see moorish designs in some cities in Spain.

_____ 7. The modern helicopter was first flown by a russian american scientist.

_____ 8. This is not a typical new england village.

_____ 9. Because it was a special dinner, we served indian food.

_____ 10. I'm very interested in middle eastern history.

WORKSHEET 5 | ## Capitalizing Proper Adjectives and School Subjects
(Rules 12 e, f)

EXERCISE Add capital letters where necessary in the following sentences by drawing a
line through each incorrect lowercase letter and writing the correct capital letter above it.
If a sentence is already correct, write *C* on the line provided.

EXAMPLE _____ 1. My grandmother is ~~e~~nglish and my grandfather

is ~~g~~erman.

_____ **1.** Was that subject covered in my social studies course?

_____ **2.** That restaurant specializes in italian cooking.

_____ **3.** Nester signed up for second-year german.

_____ **4.** We learned how to chop an onion in home economics class.

_____ **5.** Were you there when Aunt Fiona taught us how to dance a scottish fling?

_____ **6.** The bossa nova is a type of south american music.

_____ **7.** The art museum recently purchased some ancient maya sculptures.

_____ **8.** Professor Jansen is preparing her notes for a course in roman history.

_____ **9.** In college, Alfred will be majoring in english.

_____ **10.** Many scientists use mathematical reasoning to solve theoretical problems.

_____ **11.** The field trip to New Mexico will focus on navajo culture.

_____ **12.** My brother plans to take latin I during his first semester and spanish I his
second semester.

_____ **13.** I bought my father a book about mediterranean food for his birthday.

_____ **14.** Mumtaz and her family are going on an alaskan cruise next summer.

_____ **15.** Joel and Eva plan to attend a cajun festival this weekend in Louisiana.

_____ **16.** This week our english class will be studying a form of japanese poetry
known as haiku.

_____ **17.** Do you enjoy hearing about the heroic deeds in greek and roman myths?

_____ **18.** Yes, I do, and I also enjoy uncovering the moral lessons illustrated by many
african american folk tales.

_____ **19.** Numerous american indian myths describe ways that elements of the
universe were created.

_____ **20.** Folk tales and myths in different cultures often describe similar situations
and have the same themes.

LANGUAGE HANDBOOK **12** CAPITAL LETTERS

| WORSHEET 6 | Capitalizing Titles (Rule 12 g)

EXERCISE A Circle the letters that should be capitalized in each of the following sentences.

> **EXAMPLE 1.** Do you know that ⓓad wants ⓓr. ⓟarks to teach him how to ski cross-country?

1. We read *the diary of anne frank* and then saw the play.
2. The secretary of defense under president Lyndon Johnson was Robert McNamara.
3. My little brother's favorite TV program is *The magic school bus.*
4. I really like the comic strip "peanuts," don't you?
5. Have you read the story "the circuit" by Francisco Jiménez?
6. Abraham Lincoln worked closely with secretary of state William Seward.
7. After Liz saw the movie *titanic,* she kept singing the song, "my heart will go on."
8. Please tell captain Jackson that I will be ten minutes late.
9. Tomás spent the summer in Mexico with aunt Rosa.
10. Greta loved Paul Theroux's book about train travel, *the old patagonian express.*

EXERCISE B Supply all the missing capitals in each of the following sentences by crossing out each incorrect lowercase letter and writing the correct capital letter above it.

> **EXAMPLE 1.** The ⁿew ʸorker is a popular magazine.

1. In the Greek play *oedipus rex* the gods play a major role in people's lives.
2. Aunt Edna, have you seen our copy of the Sunday edition of *the news and observer?*
3. The book I am reading, *baseball is a funny game,* is very amusing.
4. At the meeting, president Polanski proposed that we sponsor a local soccer team.
5. My sister shook hands with the secretary of state last week.
6. We are going to watch uncle Leo repair the calliope from the Barnum & Bailey Circus.
7. One of Texas's most respected representatives was congresswoman Barbara Jordan.
8. Ms. Jenkins wants us to memorize "casey at the bat" for assembly.
9. When Jamaica became independent, the United States was represented at the ceremonies by vice president Johnson.
10. If you are interested in horses, I would certainly recommend *king of the wind* by Marguerite Henry.

LANGUAGE
HANDBOOK **12** CAPITAL LETTERS

WORKSHEET 7 | Test (Rules 12 a–g)

EXERCISE A   Circle the letters that should be capitalized in the following sentences.

EXAMPLES 1. Lee enjoys science and plans to take ⓒhemistry II.

2. Both ⓒatholics and non-ⓒatholics greatly admired ⓜother Teresa.

1. The african country morocco would be fun to visit.

2. We studied it in history class last year, and I learned that most moroccans are muslim.

3. From 1912 to 1956, part of morocco was divided into french and spanish zones and was ruled by those countries.

4. The kingdom is now united, with the city of rabat as its capital.

5. Would you rather have lived during the stone age, the bronze age, or the iron age?

6. Cory asked, "Should I take algebra II or geometry next year?"

7. Gunnar's parents donated new macintosh® computers for the graphics classes.

8. Felicia loves math and takes calculus 201 at the junior college on saturdays.

9. The english class is more challenging than the science class this semester.

10. Next year my electives will be art I, latin, and tennis.

11. when the bell rang, i ran to my geography II class.

12. We have an irish setter named fergus.

13. "The inn of lost time" by Lensey Namioka has a story within the story.

14. Carmen asked, "Is labor day always on a monday?"

15. Do you know the song "american pie"?

16. Where did ms. novich put the recipe for tomatillo salsa?

17. They took the train *city of new orleans* to chicago to hear jesse jackson speak.

18. Jon's uncle was awarded a nobel prize in economics last year.

19. We recited the poem "o captain! my captain!" at the fourth of july celebration.

20. We saw venus bright in the sky as we drove to the texas rangers game.

21. This weekend, we will attend the colorado state fair in pueblo.

22. Did you rent a video of the animated film *antz*?

23. Noah plans to see the washington monument during his spring break.

24. "The chair recognizes senator smith," announced chairman jones.

25. Heidi and bob rented skis at the resort in squaw valley, california.

Continued ☞

LANGUAGE HANDBOOK 12 WORKSHEET 7 (continued)

EXERCISE B Add capital letters where necessary in the following sentences by crossing out each incorrect lowercase letter and writing the correct capital letter above it. If a sentence is already correct, write *C* on the line provided.

EXAMPLE _____ 1. Have you seen my copy of *where the sidewalk ends*?

_____ 1. Thomas Jefferson was the president who negotiated the louisiana purchase.

_____ 2. One of my favorite books is Robert Louis Stevenson's *treasure island.*

_____ 3. That bearded man over there is my father.

_____ 4. Yesterday in class we read the poem "the toaster."

_____ 5. Sometimes the wind that blows off lake michigan is very cold.

_____ 6. Have you read the story "the landlady" yet?

_____ 7. My cousin is an aide to ambassador mabel smythe.

_____ 8. The city of Jerusalem is sacred to muslims, christians, and jews.

_____ 9. In 1994, Nelson Mandela was elected president of south africa.

_____ 10. One of the magazines at the dentist's office is *highlights for children.*

_____ 11. Will you be entering your strawberry preserves in this year's strawberry festival?

_____ 12. Every week we attend services at the synagogue on the corner.

_____ 13. I read in the newspaper that a grecian vase was stolen from the museum.

_____ 14. Mr. Carlyle loves to read about english history.

_____ 15. On Saturday the Garcia family took a hike along barton creek.

_____ 16. What time is your mathematics class?

_____ 17. Your appointment with Professor Wilson is on wednesday, august 15.

_____ 18. Dr. Chan has been our family doctor for years.

_____ 19. Will we be taking history II next semester?

_____ 20. My aunt Luisa is a member of the ohio state historical society.

_____ 21. The Battle of San Juan Hill was fought during the spanish-american war.

_____ 22. Did you see congresswoman waters at the press conference?

_____ 23. This year we'll be spending thanksgiving with our grandfather.

_____ 24. Boy, have I got spring fever!

_____ 25. Today I would like to announce my candidacy for the united states senate.

Continued ☞

EXERCISE C   Correct the capitalization in the paragraph below by crossing out each incorrect lowercase letter and writing the correct capital letter above it.

EXAMPLE   The culture of *A*frican *A*mericans produced the music known as jazz.

Anyone who has studied united states history knows that our country was settled by people from many lands. Not all of us, however, realize how much the customs of these other lands still influence our daily life.

A glance at a map of the united States shows some of the main foreign influences in each region's names. In the east we find many dutch names like rensselaer, brooklyn, and schenectady. In the west and southwest we find spanish names like San francisco and Nevada. In the midwest and the south, french explorers and settlers left their mark in names like La Crosse and Dubuque, Baton rouge and new Orleans.

New Orleans, indeed, is a good example of the way other cultures have affected american life. Many of its streets still bear such French names as Toulouse street and gravier street. Restaurants there are famous for their french dishes. The architecture of the French quarter, however, looks more spanish than french, reflecting many years of spanish rule.

The influences that have shaped our country turn up in some surprising places. Many of washington, d.c.'s monuments, for example, have the classic lines of a greek temple dedicated to the ancient gods. In the southeast, a few mansions built before the American civil war recall the same architecture. Some of california's churches, founded by early catholic missionaries, would be equally at home in Mexico.

America's food, too, has been influenced by many cultures. Who has not at some time enjoyed chinese egg drop soup, italian pasta, mexican tacos, or the german and scandinavian cheeses of wisconsin? The smorgasbord may seem american, but the idea originated in sweden. Pretzels were originally dutch delicacies. Shish kebab, which is often served at backyard barbecues, is actually a turkish dish. Bagels and knishes are popular jewish dishes. No thanksgiving dinner would be complete without turkey, corn, and pumpkin. These foods are truly american, for they came to us from the american Indians who lived here long before the pilgrims reached north America.

LANGUAGE HANDBOOK **13** **PUNCTUATION**

WORKSHEET 1 **Using End Marks (Rules 13 a–d)**

EXERCISE A   Add an appropriate end mark to each of the following sentences.

EXAMPLE **1.** Have you known Mr. Appleton long**?**

1. Mr. Appleton originally came from Columbia, Missouri

2. Isn't he the one who bought the old Hertzog house

3. He has spent hours in the courthouse looking up old records

4. What an interesting pastime that must be

5. History is certainly fascinating

6. Does Mr. Appleton have a regular job

7. No, he is retired and has taken up local history as a hobby

8. Would he mind if I asked him about his hobby

9. Ring his doorbell and find out

10. Mr. Appleton is very interested in the past

EXERCISE B   On the lines provided, change the statements below to questions and the questions to statements. Add the appropriate end marks to the new sentences, and make any necessary changes in wording.

EXAMPLE **1.** The fire engines are coming. *Are the fire engines coming?*

1. Someone is going to repair this typewriter. _____

_____

2. Did you say the beach is two miles from here? _____

_____

3. You will write the report tomorrow. _____

_____

_____

4. Were you waiting to see me, young man? _____

_____

_____

5. The line reaches the end of the block. _____

_____

_____

LANGUAGE HANDBOOK **13** PUNCTUATION

| WORSHEET 2 | **Using End Marks and Periods After Abbreviations (Rules 13 a–e)** |

EXERCISE A   Add an appropriate end mark to each of the following sentences.

EXAMPLE **1.** What made those tracks in the yards on Maple Street**?**

1. It's an armadillo, an animal with four feet and a tail that drags on the ground

2. Can an armadillo dig up plants and dig into anthills

3. Watch out for that one crossing the road

4. I saw one yesterday in Wanda's driveway

5. Oh, there's no need to be afraid; the armadillo is more afraid of us than we are of it

6. Did you know that some armadillos have nine bands of armor plating for protection

7. The word *armadillo* means "little armored one" in Spanish

8. They are found from Argentina through Central America and Mexico and as far north as Oklahoma

9. Dr. Garcia will give a lecture about them at the library at 10 A.M. Saturday

10. I can't wait to hear it

EXERCISE B   Add periods to the abbreviations in each of the following sentences.

EXAMPLE **1.** The street address for Custom Widgets, Inc**.** is 315 Sea Harbor Dr**.**, Orlando, Fla**.**, which is an easy drive from the airport.

1. Your appointment this Thursday at 2 P M is with Dr Vergese.

2. Have you ever read any books by J D Salinger or W H Auden?

3. The famous standing stones at Stonehenge date from 2000 B C, which is about 1100 years after the first structures at the site.

4. Please send the package to Ms B D Chan, P O Box 1138, Ann Arbor, MI 48104.

5. Which sounds better, Martin Luther King, Jr, Blvd or Martin Luther King, Jr, Ave ?

6. My brother J J has pinned to his bulletin board a picture of St Augustine, Fla, which was founded in A D 1565.

7. The author P J O'Rourke was interviewed on CNN about his opinion on the change in leadership at the UN.

8. My mother received her M D from Columbia University in New York, N Y, and she did her residency at Brackenridge Hospital in Austin, Tex.

9. Isn't Mrs Jergens a member of the Parents and Teachers Assn ?

10. The length of the curtains has been trimmed from 1 yd to 34 in so that the hem won't drag on the windowsill.

LANGUAGE HANDBOOK 13 PUNCTUATION

WORKSHEET 3 | Using Commas to Separate Words and Phrases and After Introductory Elements (Rules 13 f, g, j)

EXERCISE Punctuate the following sentences with commas where they are needed.

> **EXAMPLES** 1. Felicia bought the stereo, brought it home, and set it up.
>
> 2. Whenever she turned on the radio, the bright, clear sound pleased her.

1. Mrs. Jones stopped her car opened the door and walked to a telephone booth near the roadside.

2. For lunch we had soup salad and banana bread.

3. Where we will go when we will leave and how long we will stay are problems yet to be settled.

4. Dr. Solomon ordered bandages liniment and rest for my foot.

5. I soaked my foot rubbed it and walked very little for several days.

6. Orange juice cereal and vegetables are on the grocery list.

7. After a hot muggy afternoon we had a violent thunderstorm.

8. As long as you plan to go downtown will you pick up a train schedule at the station for me?

9. In its annual report to the public the Salt Lake City weather bureau announced that we had experienced the coldest winter since 1897.

10. The hound chased the rabbit across the meadow through the swamp and into the woods.

11. The long dark pathway led to a grim ruined house.

12. The movie was advertised as gigantic stupendous and colossal.

13. All seventh-grade eighth-grade and ninth-grade boys should report to the gym.

14. The enormous white drifting snowflakes were beautiful.

15. Skating hockey and skiing classes will begin in January.

16. After a month of beautiful weather the past three Saturdays have been windy cold and rainy.

17. We saw the biologists come back with a long scary rattlesnake.

18. Coretta found a red hand-knit ski hat for her boyfriend.

19. Our lunchroom is bright cheerful noisy and efficient.

20. Now that winter's coming I am looking for a pair of warm black gloves.

| WORSHEET 4 | **Using Commas in Compound Sentences and with Interrupters (Rules 13 h, i)** |

EXERCISE A Add commas where they are needed in the following sentences.

> **EXAMPLE 1.** I was interested in Sojourner Truth's life, but I did not know where to find information about her.

1. I did not have a book about her at home so I found one at the public library.

2. I read it some time ago yet the story stays fresh in my mind.

3. She was given the name Isabella as a child but she gave up the name eventually.

4. She chose the name Sojourner Truth for it reflected her religious beliefs.

5. Some sources say she was born in 1797 but no one knows for certain.

6. She learned about the movement to abolish slavery and she became one of the movement's most effective speakers.

7. Some might remember her best as an abolitionist or they might remember her as a women's rights advocate.

8. The stories of slaves' lives are very sad yet we should read and learn from them.

9. The struggle against slavery was hard yet Sojourner Truth never gave up.

10. She did not stop fighting for the rights of freed slaves after slavery was abolished nor did she lessen her support for women's causes.

EXERCISE B Insert commas in the following sentences to set off nonessential phrases and clauses, appositives, words used in direct address, and parenthetical expressions.

> **EXAMPLE 1.** Lewis Carroll, a well-known English author, wrote both prose and poetry.

1. The tamales just out of the pot and steaming on a platter looked too good to resist.

2. The stray cat by the way has made herself at home on our porch.

3. The championship game postponed by rain resumed last night.

4. The millpond glittering in the moonlight looked lovely.

5. If I clean my room Mother may I go to the party?

6. My uncle Cecil who was a navigator in the Air Force taught me the constellations.

7. Toni Cade Bambara one of my favorite writers once spoke at the local college.

8. Sasha don't forget to return those books to the library.

9. Our oldest dog Wilbur loves to ride in the car.

10. Amy Tan who wrote *The Joy Luck Club* was born in Oakland, California.

LANGUAGE HANDBOOK **13** **PUNCTUATION**

WORKSHEET 5 | Using Commas with Interrupters and with Introductory Words, Phrases, and Clauses (Rules 13 i, j)

EXERCISE A   Add commas where they are needed in the following sentences.

> **EXAMPLE** **1.** Burt**,** have you ever met Dr. Stearns?

1. Our newest neighbor Dr. Stearns is a veterinarian.

2. She has a marvelous gift with animals I'm sure.

3. For example even a gentle dog will bite when it is hurt.

4. The sickest dog seems to know however that Dr. Stearns is its friend.

5. Not long ago a stray dog was hit by a delivery truck on Carter Drive a street near the doctor's house.

6. Well Dr. Stearns ran out of the house when she heard the noise.

7. "Can you do anything Doc?" someone asked.

8. The dog a big yellow mongrel let her come near without a growl.

9. She took care of the dog for quite a while three months altogether.

10. The dog thank goodness experienced a full recovery.

EXERCISE B   Add commas where they are needed in the following sentences.

> **EXAMPLE** **1.** Exhausted from the workout**,** Kenta walked home slowly.

1. No I have never tried herbal tea.

2. By the time Keith and Carl had driven through the rain to Tulsa they decided not to go any farther.

3. From the depths of his vivid imagination Ray Bradbury creates fascinating stories.

4. Born and raised in a Mexican American neighborhood in Fresno Gary Soto draws on his own life for his writing.

5. After she read *The Haunting of Hill House* Millie refused to answer the door after dark.

6. As the highest peak in New England New Hampshire's Mount Washington stands 6,288 feet tall.

7. To view the three spectacular waterfalls people traveling through the Columbia River Gorge in Oregon must take the old road.

8. Well why don't you give her a call?

9. Stunned by the assassination of Martin Luther King, Jr., in 1968 many people wept.

10. Standing together after winning the championship the team happily received the cheers and applause.

WORKSHEET 6 | **Using Commas for Dates and Addresses and in Letters (Rules 13 j–k)**

EXERCISE A   Add commas where they are needed in each of the following sentences. If a sentence does not require additional commas, write *C* on the line provided.

EXAMPLE _____ 1. We need to have the project done before Sunday, March 5.

_____ 1. My sister was born on Monday February 7 1983 at 3 P.M.

_____ 2. Our town was shut down from February 1 to February 5 1993 by a blizzard.

_____ 3. The publishing company is located at 757 Third Avenue New York New York 10017.

_____ 4. The building stands on the corner of Fifth Avenue and Fiftieth Street New York City.

_____ 5. The school play will be repeated on Friday April 3 and Saturday April 4.

_____ 6. The noises came from apartment 7W.

_____ 7. Our pastor comes from a town near Pittsburgh Pennsylvania.

_____ 8. The finals will be played at Evanston Township High School Evanston Illinois.

_____ 9. Please send the book to 2107 Carney Avenue Baltimore MD 21234.

_____ 10. The project will run until November 17 2002.

_____ 11. The doctor will see you next Tuesday June 23.

_____ 12. The cookbook came from 1776 Ashland Circle Boise ID 83705.

_____ 13. The deadline fell on the afternoon of Friday August 31.

_____ 14. Will you be available next Friday afternoon?

_____ 15. The fictional detective Sherlock Holmes lived at 221B Baker Street London England.

_____ 16. There are many cable cars in the city of San Francisco.

_____ 17. The famous singer's birthplace still stands at 85 Sheridan Avenue Hohokus NJ 07423.

_____ 18. The Declaration of Independence was written in the year 1776.

_____ 19. The sporting goods shop is located at Green Acres Shopping Center Sunrise Highway Valley Stream New York.

_____ 20. Soon after 5 o'clock on Tuesday June 24 1980 we saw the meteor hit the ground.

Continued ☞

EXERCISE B   Insert the commas that are missing from the following paragraph.

EXAMPLE [1] My great-grandfather was born in Dime Box**,** Texas**,** on August 23**,** 1920.

[1] My great-great-grandfather on my father's side was born in Calhoun County South Carolina on March 2 1898. [2] He grew up in a house at 1716 Cedar Street Weldon North Carolina, in the northern part of the state. [3] My great-great-grandmother was born in Charleston South Carolina on August 23 1902. [4] As a girl, she grew up just around the corner from her future husband, at 210 East Sixth Street. [5] She was several years younger than he, however, and he never paid much attention to her until September 12 1917, just before he went off to war with the Weldon volunteers. [6] He was stationed in Paris France. [7] He came back on leave to marry his sweetheart, in New York New York. [8] They were married on Saturday December 28 1918. [9] They moved to Texas soon after my great-great-grandfather got out of the army in 1919. [10] On December 15 1928 they moved from Dime Box to the city, where they lived in the same house for the rest of their lives, at 3 Park Terrace Houston Texas.

EXERCISE C   Add commas to the following letter as needed.

EXAMPLE Please forward any packages to P.O. Box 113**,** Austin**,** TX 78704.

March 11 2000

Dear Josie

Here's my new address: 1352 Sycamore Street Fillmore TX 73214. We've been so busy! After moving into the new house we spent several days arranging and rearranging things. Yes we did get a dog from the animal shelter now that we have a fenced yard. Before we had a chance to decide on a name my little brother started calling him Bubba.

Remember not to use our old address—343 Ardmore Avenue Houston Texas—when you write.

Your friend

Anna

LANGUAGE HANDBOOK **13** PUNCTUATION

WORKSHEET 7 | **Using Semicolons and Colons (Rules 13 l–q)**

EXERCISE A   Add semicolons where necessary in the following sentences.

> **EXAMPLE 1.** Prairie dogs are not dogs; they are rodents and are members of the squirrel family.

1. There are five kinds of prairie dogs the black-tailed is the most numerous.

2. Black-tailed prairie dogs live in the plains of Mexico, Texas, New Mexico, Oklahoma, and other states white-tailed prairie dogs live in areas of Arizona, New Mexico, Utah, Colorado, and Wyoming.

3. In prairie dog country you can often see prairie dog towns every mound of dirt indicates the entrance to a prairie dog tunnel.

4. The mounds are used as lookout points that is, the prairie dogs stand on the mounds to watch for predators.

5. If a prairie dog spots a predator, it gives a high-pitched bark that warns all the prairie dogs to go underground as a result, most prairie dogs escape the danger.

6. The mounds also serve as water barriers otherwise, the burrows would flood during heavy rains.

7. In open country prairie dog tunnels may stretch for miles the tunnels can house hundreds of family groups called coteries.

8. Along the tunnels, each coterie has its own underground rooms and each room has a particular purpose, such as for sleeping, nursing babies, or storing food.

9. Baby prairie dogs stay with their parents for one year the following spring, the young leave to start families of their own.

10. Prairie dogs do not hibernate instead, they spend the winters underground living off the seeds and grasses they have stored.

EXERCISE B   Add colons where necessary in the following sentences.

> **EXAMPLE 1.** Here are two books you might enjoy: *The Hobbit,* by J. R. R. Tolkien, and *I, Robot,* by Isaac Asimov.

1. The class begins promptly at 8 30 tomorrow morning.

2. I only want to know one thing Where did you put the casserole dish?

3. Read these poems for class tomorrow "Paul Revere's Ride" and "Barbara Frietchie."

4. Both poems are in the section titled "The American Hero Myth and Reality."

5. The verse from the Bible that I want you to consider is Second Corinthians 3 6.

| WORKSHEET 8 | Test (Rules 13 a–q)

EXERCISE A   Add commas, semicolons, and end marks where they are needed in the following sentences.

EXAMPLE 1. Sarah**,** did you see my brother at the video store**?**

1. Wow Look at the size of that tiger

2. To make the posters of course we need markers water colors and stencils

3. Do you know Mandy that Jack London lived to be only forty years old

4. Above the rooftop of the apartment building we saw a beautiful bright rainbow

5. Phillip unplug the table saw right now

6. Casey and I are going to make enchiladas for the fiesta Lillian is making salsa

7. For the chalupas Patrick will make baked crisp corn tortillas

8. Let's each bring a real plate a cloth napkin and tableware so that we don't use throwaway items

9. Our fiesta will be held on September 16 2000 that is the anniversary of the beginning of the 1810 Mexican rebellion against Spain

10. We will have food games and piñatas and a folk group will sing play and dance

EXERCISE B   Add commas, semicolons, and end marks where needed in the following sentences.

EXAMPLE 1. The pool was not heated**;** nevertheless, we went swimming**.**

1. Wanting to play drums very well Logan practiced every day

2. Their mailing address has been changed to P O Box 312 Carrizozo New Mexico

3. Do you enjoy computer-animated films like *Toy Story*

4. What a brilliant meteor that is

5. Planting the seeds watering them and weeding the area usually results in healthy growth

6. Kwanzaa an African American holiday is celebrated between Dec 26 and Jan 1

7. Sonia please get off the phone

8. The tall graceful sycamore tree by our house is dying it will have to be cut down soon

9. Brer Lion listened to Brer Rabbit's advice however, he later realized he'd been tricked

10. Writer Amy Ling lives in the United States yet she was born in Beijing China

Continued ☞

EXERCISE C   Add commas, semicolons, colons, and end marks where they are needed in the following paragraph.

> **EXAMPLE** African elephants are threatened by the ivory trade**;** poachers kill the elephants for their tusks**,** which are then sold illegally**.**

One hundred years ago there were a hundred thousand elephants living in Asia however, now there are only about one third of that number What an alarming loss The Asian elephant is now an endangered species for the following reasons cutting of forests other damage to habitat and increased human population Of the Asian elephants that remain about ten thousand live in the small country of Myanmar Can you find it on a map It is between Thailand and Bangladesh Many of the huge patient elephants also called timber elephants work with humans together they bring in large valuable trees to sell for lumber Elephants and people have a partnership and they spend their lives together This partnership is remarkable for the mutual affection and trust it demonstrates between animals and humans

EXERCISE D   Add commas and end marks where they are needed in the following letter.

> **EXAMPLE** Are you interested in joining the club**?** We'd love to have you**!**

August 18 2000

Dear Nolan

Jovita told me that you are interested in joining the Environmental Club Welcome aboard Beginning Sept 10 2000 we will meet each Thursday after school at the recycling center at 1651 Yeager Ave At each meeting progress reports are given activities are discussed and plans are made We also have some social time of course and everyone enjoys the meetings The club's goal is to make our town litter-free and so far we have made a lot of progress Jovita the other members of the club and I look forward to having you as a part of our group

Sincerely

Gwynneth

Continued ☞

EXERCISE E Add commas, colons, and semicolons where they are needed to the following business letter.

> **EXAMPLE** Please send me the following items**:** a new food processor lid**,** a copy of the food processor manual**,** and a new motor.

September 5 2000

Dear Customer Service Representative

Recently I called about my food processor which has the following defects The container lid flies off when the power is turned on the speed is always fast regardless of the button pushed and smoke pours out of the motor. Your manual "Food Processors How to Enjoy Them" has not been much help at all. Although most manuals have a section that describes what to do about possible problems this manual does not.

When I called you said the manager would contact me furthermore, you said the manager would have someone from the Small Appliance Repair Department call me. Neither has happened and three months seems long enough to wait.

The food processor was purchased April 3 the problems began July 5 a few days after the ninety-day warranty expired. While I realize that these things happen your company's lack of response has had the following effect It has caused me to lose confidence in your company your company's advertising your company's reliability and your company's products.

Please contact me before I vow never to buy your company's products again.

Sincerely

Phyllis Freeman

WORKSHEET 1 | **Using Italics (Rules 14 a, b)**

EXERCISE Underline the words and phrases that should be italicized in the following sentences.

> **EXAMPLE 1.** When will our <u>Newsweek</u> subscription start?

1. That she writes a g like a q makes some words hard to read.

2. George Gershwin wrote the music for the musical Porgy and Bess.

3. Have you read Iola Fuller's novel The Loon Feather?

4. The Amtrak train Sunset Limited travels a beautiful route.

5. Can the word access be used as both a noun and a verb?

6. Picasso's painting Woman Ironing is one of his early works.

7. Which animated film did you like better, Pocahontas or Mulan?

8. When I was in Florida, I watched the space shuttle Discovery being launched.

9. Should we use the word cheap or inexpensive to describe the prices at our book sale?

10. USA Today is the newspaper many motels provide for their guests.

11. When my aunt was in California, she watched an episode of Frasier being filmed.

12. The luxury liner Queen Mary is no longer in service.

13. One of my favorite books is The Incredible Journey.

14. Did Mr. Burns show your class the video of Jack London's The Call of the Wild?

15. My brother's favorite movie about sports is Field of Dreams.

16. Janna's aunt is an opera singer and recently sang the lead in Aida.

17. Is supersede the only word that ends in sede?

18. The popularity of the recording Chant inspired several sequels.

19. Each Christmas season we attend the city ballet's performance of The Nutcracker.

20. J.R.R. Tolkien's novel The Fellowship of the Ring is the first of his well-known trilogy.

21. The play The Miracle Worker is very intense.

22. The Wright brothers' Flyer was the plane they first flew at Kitty Hawk.

23. Why is ough in cough, bough, enough, and through pronounced differently in each word?

24. Have you heard Bob Dylan's CD Time Out of Mind?

25. Shouldn't that 6 be a 9 instead?

LANGUAGE HANDBOOK 14 PUNCTUATION

WORKSHEET 2 | Punctuating Quotations (Rules 14 c–g)

EXERCISE A   Add capital letters, end marks, commas, and quotation marks where they are needed in the following sentences. If a sentence does not need any additional punctuation, write *I* for indirect quotation on the line provided.

EXAMPLES _____*I*_____ 1. Gary asked Leah why she was smiling.

                                          M
_____ 2. Leah replied, "my favorite movie was just on television."

_____ 1. What was it asked Gary.

_____ 2. It was *Babe,* the movie about an orphaned pig replied Leah.

_____ 3. Oh, I love that film exclaimed Tammy.

_____ 4. Did you know there was a sequel asked Gary.

_____ 5. Tammy said I like the original movie best.

_____ 6. I like adventure films better than comedies stated Gary.

_____ 7. Leah asked Gary if he had a favorite movie.

_____ 8. I think *Raiders of the Lost Ark* with Harrison Ford is my favorite he replied.

_____ 9. Leah inquired did you see *Gone with the Wind* on television?

_____ 10. Tammy said that it was her favorite movie of all time.

EXERCISE B   Add capital letters, end marks, commas, and quotation marks where they are needed in the following sentences.

EXAMPLE 1. "Listen, everyone," said the drama teacher. "the school play this
                                                        T
year will be *The Skin of Our Teeth.*"

1. Are you going to try out for the school play asked Dawn

2. I would love to be in it, but I'm afraid I would freeze on the stage said Imala

3. That is all the more reason for auditioning replied Dawn

4. Ernesto said you have to face your fears in order to conquer them

5. You would be perfect for the role of Sabina in *The Skin of Our Teeth* responded Dawn

6. Imala said that's the role I wanted

7. Ernesto, are you going to audition for the role of Mr. Anthropus inquired Dawn

8. I sure am exclaimed Ernesto

9. Wow, that's great because I'm trying out for the part of Mrs. Anthropus exclaimed Dawn

10. Then we may all be in the play together said Imala

WORKSHEET 3 | ## Punctuating Quotations and Dialogue (Rules 14 c–i)

EXERCISE A   In the following sentences, cross out any incorrect punctuation or lowercase letters and add any punctuation marks or capital letters that have been omitted.

> **EXAMPLE   1.** "Do we need to bring our own paddles?" Charlotte asked. "Will life preservers be provided?"

1. About how long a trip will it be, asked Charlotte.

2. It's about twelve miles, replied Paul, "we will have to prepare for an all-day trip."

3. "We'll need two adults to come with us, commented Sharon, since they will have to rent the canoes and provide supervision."

4. Ms. Roth, the supervisor of the Backwoods Canoe Club, replied "I, of course, will be glad to come." "Mr. Spenser, the mathematics teacher, canoed down that part of the river last year."

5. Should we ask Mr. Spenser to come with us asked Annette?"

6. That sounds like a good idea, said Ms. Roth, "I'll personally ask him to come."

7. "We should make a map of the area, said Dennis. We could indicate where to expect white water."

8. Charlotte added "we could also show points along the land bordering the river that would help us know where we are.

9. "We could arrange for a speaker to talk to the club about handling a canoe in white water suggested Ms. Roth.

10. My parents are excellent canoeists, said Dennis they would be glad to come to talk to us."

EXERCISE B   In the following sentences, cross out any incorrect punctuation and add any punctuation marks that have been omitted. Be sure to use a paragraph symbol (¶) whenever the speaker changes

> **EXAMPLE** "Have you ever rented a canoe?" said Paul. ¶ "No," said Charlotte, "I never have."

I propose that we take a canoe trip down the Delaware said Paul with enthusiasm. We could rent the canoes in Callicoon and paddle down to Bingham Falls. I think that's a good idea said Charlotte but how do we get the canoes back to Callicoon. That's easy said Paul. There is a series of posts along the river where we can leave the canoes. We rent them at one post and check them in at a post farther down the river. Should we schedule the trip for next week asked Bruce.

WORKSHEET 4 **Using Italics and Quotation Marks (Rules 14 a, j, k)**

EXERCISE Add quotation marks and single quotation marks where they are needed in the following sentences. Underline any word or group of words that should be in italics.

> **EXAMPLES** 1. The magazine article "Your Right to Happiness" was very inspirational.
>
> 2. The news program <u>All Things Considered</u> airs every day at dinnertime.

1. "Mother said to me, Act now," said Vincente.

2. The first chapter of the Dickens novel David Copperfield is titled I Am Born.

3. Last night Frank saw an old episode of Star Trek called The Trouble with Tribbles.

4. "Vegetarians should like the poem Point of View, shouldn't they?" asked Mr. Gable.

5. The magazine article titled Aliens Have Landed! caught my attention.

6. Annie said, "My favorite poem begins Once upon a midnight dreary."

7. O. Henry's The Ransom of Red Chief is a hilarious short story.

8. Mrs. Nelson asked us to read the poem They Have Yarns by Carl Sandburg.

9. Isn't Camp Harmony an excerpt from the book Nisei Daughter?

10. She can't remember who originally wrote and performed the song Something.

11. I believe it's on the Beatles album Abbey Road.

12. My uncle John is a correspondent for the magazine U. S. News & World Report.

13. There is an article in today's New York Times titled Metropolitan Museum Names Two New Leaders.

14. "Have you ever heard about the famous train The City of New Orleans?" asked Kathryn.

15. The famous painting Mona Lisa is on display at the Louvre in Paris, France.

16. This year the Paramount Theater is going to host a production of The Phantom of the Opera.

17. My favorite song from The Sound of Music is My Favorite Things.

18. "The poem I've Known Rivers," said Mr. Grainger, "comes from the book The Big Sea by Langston Hughes."

19. "What is the Shakespeare play," said Maria, "that includes the speech that begins Tomorrow and tomorrow and tomorrow?"

20. "I think it's Macbeth," replied Jeff.

WORKSHEET 5 Test (Rules 14 a–k)

EXERCISE A   Add quotation marks and other punctuation where they are needed in the following sentences. Circle each letter that should be capitalized.

EXAMPLE 1. Elsa asked, "ⓦhere is the party for Aaron?"

1. How many pounds are you pressing during workouts? Mom asked.

2. William, Mrs. Winters asked when will you learn?

3. The whole school will participate in Black History Month the principal said.

4. Sharon wants to take ballet Mrs. Wright said but she has twisted her ankle.

5. Ron asked, does anyone know the poem that begins A new day is dawning?

6. An old sock Andrew exclaimed is stuck in the drainpipe!

7. This German potato salad is delicious Marlene said may I have the recipe?

8. The city council voted to review the city's position Clay announced.

9. What did Jane mean asked Rachel when she said that Rose will know?

10. Marcella replied, the song is titled On Higher Ground.

EXERCISE B   On the lines provided, rewrite each of the following sentences by adding quotation marks where they are needed and removing them where they are not needed. If a sentence is already correct, write *C*.

EXAMPLE 1. Lu said, Your pictures of the ranch are beautiful. *Lu said,*
"Your pictures of the ranch are beautiful."

2. I told her that "I couldn't come to the party." *I told her*
that I couldn't come to the party.

1. Indeed, Miss Bursa replied, the Japanese yen is rising. _____

_____

2. People are generally quite hopeful, the speaker said. _____

_____

3. The governor said that Puerto Rico might become a state. _____

_____

Continued ☞

LANGUAGE HANDBOOK **14** **WORKSHEET 5** *(continued)*

4. Paul said that "the train doesn't stop here anymore." _____

_____

_____

5. Laws are for your protection, the police officer said, not your inconvenience. _____

_____

_____

6. Cody Ray said that "the story of the laughing fence post is a myth." _____

_____

_____

7. Joanne asked us whether or not we wanted to go snorkeling. _____

_____

_____

8. The game's on, rain or shine! Trevor yelled. _____

_____

_____

9. Mr. Lindt suggested "that we try out for the debate team." _____

_____

_____

10. I know the community will help the family, Reverend Marshall said. _____

_____

_____

EXERCISE C   On the lines provided, rewrite the following conversation in correct paragraph form and add quotation marks as needed. Note: There should be ten paragraphs.

EXAMPLE   Have you ever had a bagel? Rachel asked. No, said Diane, I haven't. Is it good?

"Have you ever had a bagel?" Rachel asked.

"No," said Diane, "I haven't. Is it good?"

You said your parents own a kosher deli, Rachel. What does that mean? Diane asked. It means that it's a Jewish deli, Rachel replied. Yes, I understand that. But what is *kosher*? Diane asked. Oh, it means that some food is prepared in certain ways, Rachel said. How? Diane asked. According to what standards? Jewish religious rules say how some food is to

Continued ☞

be prepared, Rachel explained. There are special recipes. Sounds interesting! Diane said. What are some of the foods that I could buy at the deli? Well, I will tell you my favorite thing to get, Rachel said. I love potato knishes! I've never had them, or even heard of them, Diane said. What are they? They're pastries filled with potatoes. I'll treat you to one after school today, Rachel said.

_____

_____

_____

_____

_____

_____

_____

_____

_____

_____

EXERCISE D   Add underlining or quotation marks as needed in the following sentences.

EXAMPLE 1. Did you see the "Big Cats" episode of <u>Nature</u>?

1. Diego Rivera's expressive painting The Grinder depicts a woman making tortillas.

2. Barbara won't leave home without her Rand McNally Road Atlas.

3. Ogden Nash, in his poem The Panther, created the word anther.

4. The song Tomorrow is from the Broadway musical Annie.

5. I clipped the article Reuse or Recycle from today's Kansas City Star for our talk.

6. In Jules Verne's novel Twenty Thousand Leagues Under the Sea, the submarine is named the Nautilus.

7. When taking notes, some people distinguish between the capital letter O and the numeral 0 by drawing a / through the numeral.

8. Toni Cade Bambara's book Gorilla, My Love has many wonderful short stories in it.

9. Some people pronounce short e's and i's the same in words like pin and pen.

10. Have you seen the dance production called Stomp?

LANGUAGE HANDBOOK **15** PUNCTUATION

WORKSHEET 1 | Using Apostrophes to Show Possession (Rule 15 a)

EXERCISE A In the first blank, write the singular possessive form of each word. In the second blank, write the plural possessive form of the same word. Make sure the placement of your apostrophe is clear.

		Singular		**Plural**	
EXAMPLE	1. teacher	*teacher's*	desk	*teachers'*	desks

	Singular		**Plural**	
1. dog	_____	tail	_____	tails
2. son	_____	smile	_____	smiles
3. cat	_____	eye	_____	eyes
4. sister	_____	task	_____	tasks
5. detective	_____	question	_____	questions
6. house	_____	chimney	_____	chimneys
7. doctor	_____	car	_____	cars
8. neighbor	_____	yard	_____	yards
9. baby	_____	bottle	_____	bottles
10. mouse	_____	squeak	_____	squeaks

EXERCISE B Add apostrophes where they are needed in the following sentences. Some sentences may have more than one apostrophe.

EXAMPLE 1. The deer's coat was speckled with sunlight.

1. Rachels and Pauls papers are on Miss Conways desk, but ours aren't.

2. One of the boys had lost his fathers jacket.

3. What shall we do with the geeses feathers?

4. In the Middle Ages a gooses feathers were used to make arrows.

5. A pelicans beak is more than a foot long, and a pouch hangs from the lower part of the beak.

6. Our grandparents old schoolbooks look dull compared with todays.

7. Please tell me the companys address.

8. What have they predicted for tomorrows weather?

9. He is so quick that he does about eight hours work in three hours.

10. Our towns oldest house is out on the river road.

LANGUAGE HANDBOOK 15 PUNCTUATION

WORKSHEET 2 | Using Apostrophes for Contractions, Plurals, and Possessives (Rules 15 a–c)

EXERCISE A On the line provided, write out the two words for which each of the following contractions stands.

EXAMPLE 1. I'm _____ *I am* _____

1. you're _____
2. she'd _____
3. didn't _____
4. wasn't _____
5. don't _____

6. isn't _____
7. we're _____
8. hasn't _____
9. he'll _____
10. you'll _____

EXERCISE B On the line provided, write the contraction for each of the following groups of words or dates.

EXAMPLE 1. she is _____ *she's* _____

1. are not _____
2. it is _____
3. she will _____
4. there is _____
5. they are _____

6. he would _____
7. let us _____
8. where is _____
9. 1970 _____
10. we would _____

EXERCISE C Underline the correct italicized word in parentheses.

EXAMPLE 1. Al, here is (*you're*, *your*) pencil.

1. Does that tree shed (*it's, its*) leaves?

2. Both men think (*they're, their*) going to win that golf match.

3. They have started (*they're, their*) game.

4. (*Who's, Whose*) voice do I hear?

5. Are you the one (*who's, whose*) singing?

6. (*It's, Its*) time to go home.

7. (*You're, Your*) the only one who can beat me in basketball free throws.

8. May I borrow (*you're, your*) sweater?

9. (*It's, Its*) becoming quite chilly.

10. The explorers have lost (*they're, their*) way.

Continued ☞

EXERCISE D   For each of the following sentences, insert apostrophes where they are needed.

> **EXAMPLE** **1.** The word *Mississippi* has four *s*'s and two *p*'s in it.

1. There are two *c*s and two *r*s in the word *occurring*.

2. Wherever we have lived, there have always been two *6*s in our address.

3. Some authors prefer to use *&*s instead of *and*s in their titles.

4. Try not to use too many *well*s in your speech.

5. Two *o*s give Geronimo's name an interesting sound.

6. Ellen's Social Security number contains four *7*s.

7. How many *@*s are in an e-mail address?

8. "Your *e*s look too much like your *i*s, Randall," said Ms. Yang.

9. Four *the*s in your title are too many, in my opinion.

10. Counting by *9*s is difficult even for some adults.

EXERCISE E   Add apostrophes where they are needed in the following sentences. Some sentences may have more than one apostrophe.

> **EXAMPLE** **1.** Getting the pond, the waterfall, and the back yard ready for the garden tour will require at least a week's work

1. My oldest brothers pet mice are as big as yours.

2. There are two pairs of mens overalls hanging behind the barn door.

3. Marie didn't give the problem a moments thought.

4. The mayors friends formed a citizens committee to reelect her.

5. Have you seen todays newspapers anywhere?

6. Ralphs bicycle is in better condition than theirs are.

7. Someone left the dogs leash on the front porch.

8. The childrens toys were scattered behind the sofa.

9. Our citys tallest buildings have all been built recently.

10. The twins mother has won an award for her story.

LANGUAGE HANDBOOK **15** PUNCTUATION

WORKSHEET 3 Using Hyphens (Rules 15 d, e)

EXERCISE A   On the line provided, show where each of the following words can be divided at the end of a line. If a word cannot be divided, simply write the word on the line.

EXAMPLES **1.** fiber _____ *fi-ber* _____

2. topsy-turvy ___ *topsy-turvy* ___

1. chopsticks _____
2. darling _____
3. Germany _____
4. position _____
5. sphinx _____
6. brother-in-law _____
7. kite _____
8. technical _____
9. Persian _____
10. cement _____

EXERCISE B   On the line provided, add hyphens where they are needed in each of the following word groups. If a word group is already correct, write *C*.

EXAMPLE **1.** in sixty one days ___ *in sixty-one days* ___

1. for thirty three years _____
2. vote of two thirds _____
3. every fifty five minutes _____
4. only one half liter _____
5. one fourth full _____
6. for seventy-eight years _____
7. received one fourth _____
8. the age of nineteen _____
9. two thirds cup _____
10. with forty one dollars _____

Elements of Literature

WORKSHEET 4 | **Using Parentheses and Dashes (Rules 15 f, g)**

EXERCISE   Add parentheses or dashes where needed in each of the following sentences. Some sentences may be punctuated with either dashes or parentheses.

EXAMPLES **1.** The Declaration of Independence (1776) is a powerful document.

2. Here comes ⁀wait, I'll let her introduce herself!

1. Tell me I doubt that you can what city is the capital of Wyoming.

2. Gouda pronounced gou´də is a kind of cheese.

3. The correct answer appears to be no, figure it out for yourself.

4. Sludge the word itself sounds horrid filled our basement during the flood.

5. Movie producer Samuel Goldwyn 1882–1974 was born in Poland.

6. Brenda can't that is, won't help me.

7. The box contains a pound 16 ounces of detergent.

8. Cajun music how I love it! is loud and lively.

9. Gila monsters they give me the shivers aren't really monsters.

10. They are classified as lizards the biological family Helodermatidae.

11. My desk calendar it was a gift contains animal cartoons.

12. "Next we will read please stop talking from the book," Mr. Naylor said.

13. My grandfather's first truck a Chevrolet is worth a lot now.

14. The right solution to your problem I repeat will come to you.

15. The winning number is but first, a commercial break.

16. The marching band can you believe it? actually won first place.

17. Derek I think you've met him enjoys racing automobiles.

18. My dream I don't care if you do laugh is to be a professional clown.

19. San Marino population 24,000 is a small independent country.

20. The restored house it has always been a favorite of mine is now a museum.

21. This picture is of a three-toed sloth species *Bradypus*.

22. Sloths believe it or not feed while hanging down from branches.

23. Khalil Gibran 1883–1931 was a writer and artist from Lebanon.

24. Have patience easier said than done and you'll succeed.

25. One of our cats the gray one often hid under the couch.

LANGUAGE HANDBOOK **15** PUNCTUATION

| WORSHEET 5 | Test (Rules 15 a–g)

EXERCISE A For each of the following words, add an apostrophe where it is needed. Then, on the line provided, identify the word as *CON* for contraction, *POS* for possessive case, or *PL* for plural. If there is more than one word in an item, identify the word in italics.

EXAMPLE ___*CON*___ 1. won't

_____ 1. shes

_____ 2. 5s

_____ 3. geeses

_____ 4. shouldnt

_____ 5. theyre

_____ 6. *foxs* den

_____ 7. whos

_____ 8. summer of *99*

_____ 9. wasnt

_____ 10. recite your *abcs*

_____ 11. two *monkeys* food

_____ 12. *Rovers* doghouse

_____ 13. *its* snowing

_____ 14. one *girls* uniform

_____ 15. 6s and 7s

_____ 16. youre

_____ 17. *familys* trip

_____ 18. many *voters* rights

_____ 19. youll

_____ 20. *thats* right

_____ 21. dot those *is* and *js*

_____ 22. *fishs* habitat

_____ 23. *nobodys* fault

_____ 24. *heres* the food

_____ 25. *childrens* playground

Continued ☞

Elements of Literature

EXERCISE B   On the line provided, write the possessive form of each word.

EXAMPLE **1.** book _____ *book's* _____

1. boy _____
2. men _____
3. persons _____
4. books _____
5. oxen _____
6. moose _____
7. poet _____
8. children _____
9. animals _____
10. year _____

11. everybody _____
12. mother _____
13. students _____
14. churches _____
15. Ross _____
16. artists _____
17. countries _____
18. videos _____
19. someone _____
20. sheep _____

EXERCISE C   On the line provided, for each of the following sentences, write the contraction that may be used in place of the italicized words.

EXAMPLE ___*She'll*___ **1.** *She will* be right back.

_____ **1.** *We had* hoped to leave by now.

_____ **2.** *It will* turn out all right.

_____ **3.** John *is not* late today.

_____ **4.** *It is* only eight o'clock.

_____ **5.** *You had* better hurry.

_____ **6.** The print in this book *does not* appear to be as small as the print in that one.

_____ **7.** *Where is* my yellow book bag?

_____ **8.** I hope the weather *will not* prevent us from having a picnic Saturday afternoon.

_____ **9.** *They had* hoped to return by 5:00 P.M. so they could finish studying before dinner.

_____ **10.** *Have* you *not* proofread your essay?

Continued ☞

LANGUAGE HANDBOOK **15** **WORKSHEET 5** *(continued)*

EXERCISE D On the line provided, correct the hyphenation of each of the following words. If a word is already correctly hyphenated, write *C*.

EXAMPLE 1. telep-hone _____*tele-phone*_____

1. pers-onal _____
2. for-ge _____
3. music-al _____
4. meas-ure _____
5. bro-ther-in-law _____
6. carr-ot _____
7. monk-ey _____
8. extremel-y _____
9. passeng-er _____
10. mot-her _____

EXERCISE E Add parentheses or dashes where needed in each of the following sentences. Some sentences may be punctuated with either dashes or parentheses.

EXAMPLE 1. That horse—Jim's horse—is fast, I guess.

1. Pesto pronounced pes´tō is a sauce made with basil, garlic, pine nuts, and olive oil.
2. "We are leaving on the 12:45 no, 1:45 P.M. flight to Chicago," John said.
3. I like the long, hooded cloaks called *burnooses* worn by some Arabs.
4. The clock its chiming drives me crazy was a gift.
5. The Dales correct me if I am wrong are on vacation.
6. Easter Island also known as Rapa Nui is inhabited by about two thousand people.
7. The star of the concert you would have loved him was the jazz saxophonist.
8. Frances Perkins was U.S. Secretary of Labor 1933–1945 under Franklin Roosevelt.
9. The next assignment will be where is my book?
10. The winter solstice the shortest day of the year ended with a beautiful sunset.

LANGUAGE HANDBOOK 16 SPELLING

| WORKSHEET 1 | **Using Word Parts**

EXERCISE   Divide each of the following words into parts (prefixes, roots, and suffixes), and write a definition based on the meanings of the parts. Check your definition in a dictionary.

EXAMPLE   1. transport _trans | port:_   _carry across_ _____

1. mislead _____

2. import _____

3. diffuse _____

4. retry _____

5. attraction _____

6. dislike _____

7. postscript _____

8. fearful _____

9. porter _____

10. spectator _____

11. distrust _____

12. misplace _____

13. diction _____

14. export _____

15. temperament _____

16. restate _____

17. healthful _____

18. disqualify _____

19. replace _____

20. portable _____

21. transcribe _____

22. respect _____

23. cheerful _____

24. translator _____

25. formation _____

LANGUAGE HANDBOOK 16 SPELLING

| WORKSHEET 2 | **Spelling Words with *ie, ei, cede, ceed,* and *sede* (Rules 16 a–c)** |

EXERCISE A Fill in the blanks with the correct letters: *ie, ei, cede, ceed,* or *sede.*

EXAMPLE 1. bel_*ie*_ve

1. rec_____pt
2. t_____
3. pro_____
4. sc_____nce
5. l_____sure
6. defic_____nt
7. se_____
8. v_____w
9. h_____ght
10. rel_____ve

11. ach_____vement
12. _____ther
13. perc_____ve
14. ex_____
15. inconc_____vable
16. super_____
17. w_____rd
18. inter_____
19. n_____ce
20. n_____gh

EXERCISE B Some of the following sentences contain spelling errors involving the use of *ie, ei, cede, ceed,* or *sede.* For each sentence, draw a line through any misspelled words and write the misspelled word correctly on the line provided. If a sentence is already correct, write *C.*

EXAMPLE ___*friendly*___ 1. Peanuts the cat was ~~freindly~~ to only a few visitors.

_____ 1. Did Whoopi Goldberg's new movie premeire in Los Angeles or New York?

_____ 2. You must wait pateintly for your turn to ride.

_____ 3. The calm preceeds the storm, according to the old saying.

_____ 4. Several pieces of the puzzle were missing.

_____ 5. Niether the lions nor the giraffes were in view this morning at the animal park.

_____ 6. Erin wants to succede in her efforts to improve her math skills.

_____ 7. The sound of a frieght train during the night is soothing.

_____ 8. This store carries foriegn-language dictionaries for Vietnamese, Burmese, and Bengali.

_____ 9. The governor finally conceded that her opponent had won.

_____ 10. You look as if the wieght of the world is on your shoulders.

Elements of Literature

LANGUAGE HANDBOOK **16** SPELLING

WORKSHEET 3 — Adding Prefixes and Suffixes (Rules 16 d–j)

EXERCISE A   On the line provided, rewrite each of the following words with the given prefix or suffix. You may have to add, drop, or change some of the letters.

EXAMPLE   **1.** total + ly = _____*totally*_____

1. outrage + ous = _____

2. sleepy + ly = _____

3. stray + ed = _____

4. mis + state = _____

5. day + ly = _____

6. normal + ly = _____

7. box + ing = _____

8. dry + ing = _____

9. il + logical = _____

10. tune + less = _____

11. rot + en = _____

12. argue + ment = _____

13. knit + ing = _____

14. over + rule = _____

15. dive + ing = _____

16. busy + ly = _____

17. frank + ness = _____

18. buy + ing = _____

19. tardy + ness = _____

20. bare + ly = _____

EXERCISE B   Some of the following sentences contain spelling errors involving the use of prefixes or suffixes. For each sentence, draw a line through any misspelled words and write the misspelled word correctly on the line provided. If a sentence contains no misspelled words, write *C*.

EXAMPLE   _____*happily*_____   **1.** The kindergarten children ~~happyly~~ bounded out of the classroom.

_____ **1.** Congress may overide the veto because the public favors the bill.

_____ **2.** The sculpture was quite noticable on the museum lawn.

_____ **3.** "The idea for the story occurred to me in the shower," Dr. Weiss said.

_____ **4.** For the ninth year, our band is leadding the Saint Patrick's Day parade.

_____ **5.** The night the accident happenned, it had been raining heavily.

_____ **6.** The baby raccoons that come to the porch are adoreable.

_____ **7.** The geology museum is giveing an amber bead to every new member.

_____ **8.** Carl and Les hurryed to the swimming pool, but it was already closed.

_____ **9.** Eveness of temper is a good character trait, don't you think?

_____ **10.** The lead dancer in the production had a catlike grace.

LANGUAGE HANDBOOK **16** SPELLING

WORKSHEET 4 | **Forming the Plurals of Nouns (Rules 16 k–v)**

EXERCISE A   On the line provided, spell the plural form of each of the following nouns, letters, symbols, or numbers.

EXAMPLE **1.** Monday _____ *Mondays* _____

1. wife _____

2. ox _____

3. raceway _____

4. Japanese _____

5. candle _____

6. county _____

7. *z* _____

8. wish _____

9. child _____

10. Cary _____

11. rodeo _____

12. two-year-old _____

13. box _____

14. Zorro _____

15. *4* _____

16. son-in-law _____

17. Johnson _____

18. potato _____

19. navy _____

20. % _____

EXERCISE B   Some of the following sentences contain spelling errors involving the plurals of nouns. For each sentence, draw a line through any misspelled word and write the misspelled word correctly on the line provided. If a sentence is already correct, write *C*.

EXAMPLE _____ *series* _____ **1.** The school is offering two ~~serieses~~ of computer classes.

_____ **1.** While digging near the old corral, I found three rusty horsesshoe.

_____ **2.** Plastic dishes are convenient to take on picnics and camping trips.

_____ **3.** Are both of your sister-in-laws still in college?

_____ **4.** The shapes of leafs are often very beautiful.

_____ **5.** The podiatrist said that most people don't treat their foots well.

_____ **6.** The Chineses have used acupuncture to relieve pain for many years.

_____ **7.** Jesse Mercado started the family business, Mercadoes, Inc.

_____ **8.** The children hung from the bars like monkeies on trees.

_____ **9.** The group honored the heroes for their bravery.

_____ **10.** "Great-sounding stereoes don't cost as much as they used to," Marge said.

LANGUAGE HANDBOOK **16** **SPELLING**

WORSHEET 5	**More Practice Forming the Plurals of Nouns and Spelling Numbers (Rules 16 k–y)**

EXERCISE A   On the line provided, spell the plural form of each of the following nouns.

EXAMPLES **1.** tax _____*taxes*_____

2. *if* _____*if's*_____

1. mouse _____

2. city _____

3. soprano _____

4. wrench _____

5. thirteen-year-old _____

6. Wiley _____

7. brief _____

8. *hello* _____

9. tomato _____

10. lily _____

11. butterfly _____

12. topaz _____

13. Vietnamese _____

14. Nero _____

15. spacecraft _____

16. man _____

17. life _____

18. igloo _____

19. galley _____

20. sit-up _____

EXERCISE B   Some of the following sentences contain errors involving the plurals of nouns and the spelling of numbers. For each sentence, write the misspelled word correctly on the line provided. If a sentence is already correct, write *C*.

EXAMPLE ____*days*____ **1.** The first few dayes at a new school are usually the most difficult.

_____ **1.** The school has won many trophys for academic contests.

_____ **2.** "At least the raines are good for the crops and for raising the water table," Malcolm said.

_____ **3.** Mrs. Lear warned, "Don't dig your ditchs too deep."

_____ **4.** The talented dance troupe performs both waltzs and break dancing.

_____ **5.** Grandfather's Boy Scout knives are still in excellent condition.

_____ **6.** The covers of the notebooks come in 2 colors, orange and green.

_____ **7.** Be sure to put four *s'* in *Mississippi.*

_____ **8.** Molly is the 3rd of four children in her family.

_____ **9.** Mr. Harrison said that 206 people applied for the job, but only 103 filled out the application form correctly.

_____ **10.** 100 years ago, the railroad obtained rights of way through the homesteads.

Elements of Literature

LANGUAGE HANDBOOK 16 SPELLING

WORKSHEET 6 Test (Rules 16 a–y)

EXERCISE A Some of the following sentences contain errors in spelling. For each sentence, draw a line through any misspelled words and write the misspelled word correctly on the line provided. If a sentence is already correct, write *C*.

EXAMPLE ___*friends*___ **1.** Do you remember your best ~~freinds~~ in kindergarten or first grade?

_____ **1.** Mr. Welch had to interceed when the two girls began arguing.

_____ **2.** "Wow, those axs are heavy!" Morgan exclaimed.

_____ **3.** Neither of the cans opener could be depended on to work.

_____ **4.** Are the Dakota peoples also known as Sioux?

_____ **5.** Strong allys can strengthen a nation.

_____ **6.** The toy airplane that Uncle Fritz made contains interchangable parts.

_____ **7.** The article stated that the weight lifter looked as strong as two ox.

_____ **8.** The vocabularies in the 2 books varied greatly.

_____ **9.** "Those seventh-graders seem so young," Felicia said, "but we were their age last year."

_____ **10.** Volcanoes are classified as active, dormant, or extinct.

EXERCISE B The following paragraph contains ten spelling errors. For each sentence, draw a line through any misspelled words and write the misspelled word correctly on the line provided on page 169.

EXAMPLE [1] Please ~~procede~~ to tell us about the Regional Art Club.

1. _____*proceed*_____

[1] The Regional Art Club includes members from middle schools in 22 cities. [2] Art critics throughout the state conceed that our members are extremely talented. [3] "Use your imagination" and "Express your creativeity" are our bywords. [4] We have large studioes at four centrally located schools. [5] There is a large vareity of artistic styles among our members. [6] Some studentes make huge sculptures out of metal objects. [7] The club is overun with painters, as you might expect. [8] Potters easly come in

Continued ☞

Elements of Literature

LANGUAGE HANDBOOK 16 WORKSHEET 6 (continued)

second in number. [9] Photography is also a popular art, especially with many students in the 9th grade. [10] Members usually meet once during the week and again on Saturdayes.

1. _____
2. _____
3. _____
4. _____
5. _____
6. _____
7. _____
8. _____
9. _____
10. _____

EXERCISE C   Some of the following sentences contain errors in spelling. For each sentence, draw a line through any misspelled words and write the misspelled word correctly on the line provided. If a sentence is already correct, write *C*.

EXAMPLE   _courageous_   1. The ~~couragous~~ girl rescued the baby from the rushing water.

_____ 1. Which one of the patioes should we sweep first?

_____ 2. The men loaded the supplys onto the truck and drove off noisily.

_____ 3. 15 members of our class paid to go to Mexico City this spring.

_____ 4. Our neighbors still observe the anceint custom of the Japanese tea ceremony.

_____ 5. You can have these sunglasses because they are too big for me.

_____ 6. World War II aircrafts are stored and displayed at the two bases.

_____ 7. The drawings depict the importance of horses to the Plains peoples.

_____ 8. My brother-in-laws seemed to enjoy the experience of chess competition.

_____ 9. In my opinion, tin rooves add a noticeable, old-fashioned charm to houses.

_____ 10. The automobile superceded the horse and carriage.

Continued ☞

LANGUAGE HANDBOOK **16** **WORKSHEET 6** *(continued)*

EXERCISE D The following paragraph contains ten spelling errors. For each sentence, draw a line through any misspelled word and write the misspelled word or words correctly on the line provided. If a sentence is already correct, write *C*.

EXAMPLE [1] The entertainer Bill Cosby is an ~~acheiver~~!

1. _____*achiever*_____

[1] Cosby has certainly succeded in many areas. [2] Cosby was one of three boys in a Philadelphia family. [3] Even as a boy, Cosby told storys that amused people. [4] Happyly for his many fans, he has had a long, successful career. [5] Cosby has stared in hit situation comedys and television dramas. [6] He has recieved several awards for his acting. [7] *The Cosby Show* is one of my favorite serieses. [8] Cosby wrote about parentting in the popular book *Fatherhood.* [9] He is also one of the most educated mans in show business. [10] He truely can be called "Dr. Cosby," because he has a Ph.D. in education.

1. _____
2. _____
3. _____
4. _____
5. _____
6. _____
7. _____
8. _____
9. _____
10. _____

Elements of Literature

LANGUAGE HANDBOOK 17 GLOSSARY OF USAGE

| WORKSHEET 1 | **Common Usage Problems**

EXERCISE   Underline the word or expression in parentheses that is correct according to standard or formal usage.

> EXAMPLE **1.** Deciding (*between*, *among*) these two movies is difficult.

1. Simon hoped there would be (*fewer*, *less*) questions on the test about bones and muscles in the body.

2. The cat has pneumonia and still does not look (*good*, *well*).

3. You (*ought*, *had ought*) to wear something dressy for the job interview.

4. Ms. (*Jones*, *Jones she*) helped the youth of the Chicago area.

5. "(*Alot*, *A lot*) of people don't like algebra, but it's my best subject," Joanne said.

6. Country music is much more popular in our community (*than*, *then*) any other form of music.

7. (*A*, *An*) Gila monster, a type of desert lizard, isn't truly a monster.

8. The house-cleaning chores were divided (*between*, *among*) the three children.

9. Years ago my Paiute ancestors (*chose*, *choose*) to move from southern Utah.

10. Gretchen talked (*like*, *as if*) she wanted to go to the beach with us tomorrow.

11. Laura has never had piano lessons and, to be honest, plays quite (*bad*, *badly*).

12. The library now has a (*real*, *very*) interesting book of Vietnamese legends.

13. The reason we received no e-mail today is (*because*, *that*) the server has been down.

14. The sled is (*inside of*, *inside*) the garage but behind stacks of boxes.

15. The clown put (*hisself*, *himself*) in an awkward situation with that joke.

16. Mrs. Graves (*taught*, *learned*) us that the Panama Canal connects the Caribbean Sea and the Gulf of Panama.

17. The company report concludes that there (*ain't*, *isn't*) much demand for orange wigs.

18. Cheryl's backpack zipper (*busted*, *broke*) while she was on her way to school.

19. "I am surprised (*some*, *somewhat*) that you've never eaten lentil soup," Benjamin said.

20. Probably everyone (*accept*, *except*) Eliza is hoping for more snow.

21. The politician's appearance had a beneficial (*affect*, *effect*) on the fund-raiser.

22. Sabrina was not (*altogether*, *all together*) certain that she wanted to go.

23. You (*hadn't ought*, *ought not*) to have had a second helping of food.

24. Will Aaron tell you (*how come*, *why*) he didn't attend the party?

25. The rally organizers were (*sort of*, *somewhat*) upset by the low turnout.

| WORSHEET 2 | **Common Usage Problems**

EXERCISE Underline the word or expression in parentheses that is correct according to standard or formal usage.

> EXAMPLE **1.** The weather definitely (_affects_, _effects_) some people's moods.

1. More people could (_of_, _have_) gone to the game if it had been on a weekend night.

2. "I (_kind of_, _rather_) wanted to go to my friend's wedding, but I was out of town," Carla said.

3. My mother's new perfume smells (_badly_, _bad_), in my opinion.

4. At this point no one really knows what (_affects_, _effects_) the new discovery will have on astronomy.

5. There is (_fewer_, _less_) water in the pond now because of the drought.

6. Poco wanted to know why Tasha gave (_them_, _those_) sweaters away.

7. Do you know (_why_, _how come_) totem poles are often painted brightly?

8. We are fortunate to be able to (_chose_, _choose_) which classes to take.

9. When the employees were (_all together_, _altogether_), the manager began the meeting.

10. Working (_good_, _well_) with others is one trait of an outstanding employee.

11. (_Advertisers_, _Advertisers they_) often use the persuasive technique of exaggeration.

12. (_Like_, _As_) you may know, tofu, an Asian food, is made from soybeans.

13. Did you read (_where_, _that_) the pool will close at 6 P.M. Saturday?

14. Has Shawn (_already_, _all ready_) resigned as director of the theater troupe?

15. The (_busted_, _burst_) pipe flooded the carpet throughout the house.

16. Dad and I will (_try and_, _try to_) dig all of the weeds out of the garden and flower beds.

17. A truant is (_when a pupil_, _a pupil who_) stays out of school without permission.

18. Lou wasn't certain where Grafton Street (_is_, _is at_).

19. We were shocked when the twins helped (_theirselves_, _themselves_) to two servings of everything.

20. The sparrow quickly flew (_off of_, _off_) the branch when the cat appeared.

21. Habañero peppers are hotter (_then_, _than_) jalapeño peppers.

22. Caroline's tennis serve improved (_some_, _somewhat_) with practice.

23. Mrs. Brown tried to (_learn_, _teach_) the eighth-graders about prime factors.

24. When my sister is sad, she gets (_very_, _real_) quiet.

25. We might (_have_, _of_) made our decision earlier, but we needed more facts.

LANGUAGE HANDBOOK **17** GLOSSARY OF USAGE

WORKSHEET 3 | Test

EXERCISE A Underline the word or expression in parentheses that is correct according to standard or formal usage.

> **EXAMPLE 1.** (*Them,* *Those*) new boots will keep your feet warm in the winter.

1. To our astonishment, the ball landed (*outside, outside of*) the court.

2. "I've (*all ready, already*) heard enough of your excuses," Mr. Lindt said sternly.

3. Some of my (*friends, friends they*) are fasting for Yom Kippur.

4. After the engine was repaired, its performance was improved (*some, somewhat*).

5. Is the play worth seeing, (*like, as*) the reviewers proclaim?

6. The poncho that I bought at the Mexican market is made (*good, well*).

7. Chipmunks belong to a different species (*than, then*) squirrels.

8. Laverne's earring fell (*between, among*) the boards of the porch floor.

9. Some, but not all, classical music has a peaceful (*affect, effect*) on listeners.

10. The amount of Ted's check was (*fewer, less*) than he thought it would be.

EXERCISE B Most of the following sentences contain errors in usage. For each sentence, draw a line through the error and then correct it on the line provided. If a sentence is already correct, write *C*.

> **EXAMPLE** ____*a lot*____ **1.** The respect of friends means ~~alot~~ to most people.

_____ **1.** The runner tripped on a rock at the start of the race and turned her ankle bad.

_____ **2.** I must of heard that story fifty times, but it still makes me cry.

_____ **3.** Chen explained how come Chinese writing looks so distinctive.

_____ **4.** The speaker, a famous chemist, has a real dignified appearance.

_____ **5.** The principal listened like he really wanted to know my concerns and feelings.

_____ **6.** Yesterday our teacher taught us that hydrogen is the most common element.

_____ **7.** The young hero excepted the community award with true humility.

_____ **8.** The garlic bagels at the new shop are all together delicious.

_____ **9.** Where in Massachusetts was the author Edgar Allan Poe born at?

_____ **10.** The reason the dog is barking is because there are three opossums in the garage.

Continued ☞

EXERCISE C   Underline the word or expression in parentheses that is correct according to standard or formal usage.

EXAMPLE 1. Whom did you (*chose*, <u>*choose*</u>) as your partner for the project?

1. The diners complained to the waiter that the eggplant tasted (*bad, badly*).

2. Have you read (*where, that*) Langston Hughes began writing poems as a teenager?

3. Aunt Pearl recovered (*good, well*) after the surgery and healed quickly.

4. The rearview mirror (*busted, broke*) when the side of the truck brushed a bridge railing.

5. (*A, An*) opal can refract and reflect light beautifully.

6. The organizers of the concert (*should of, should have*) anticipated a bigger crowd for the band.

7. We are (*already, all ready*) for our trip to the amusement park.

8. French berets have become popular at school, but I (*ain't, am not*) wearing one.

9. The sisters promised (*theirselves, themselves*) that they always would remain friends.

10. Anyone who writes a book report will be (*accepted, excepted*) from taking the reading test.

EXERCISE D   Most of the following sentences contain errors in usage. For each sentence, draw a line through the error and then correct it on the line provided. If a sentence is already correct, write *C*.

EXAMPLE ____*fewer*____ 1. This cave has ~~less~~ stalagmites than the last one we toured.

_____ 1. The boys busted a serving dish in the kitchen.

_____ 2. Bermuda onions are large but have a sort of mild flavor.

_____ 3. Barter is when there is an exchange of goods.

_____ 4. Let's try to bike to the river and back in an hour.

_____ 5. El Niño sometimes effects the weather drastically.

_____ 6. The judges obviously were having difficulty deciding between the four skaters.

_____ 7. Monroe bought himself a new watch with money from mowing yards.

_____ 8. Jane was kind of upset when she discovered her books were missing.

_____ 9. The Hawaiian host choose a beautiful lei to place around Nanna's neck.

_____ 10. We hadn't ought to let worries fill our thoughts, but we often do.